THE CRAZIEST GAMBLE

THE
CRAZIEST
GAMBLE

TREVOR & IRIS LIDDLE

10 Travers Street, New Herrington, Houghton- Le-Spring
Tyne & Wear, DH4 7AA, UK

Published in Great Britain 2007 by
T. and I. Liddle, 10 Travers Street, New Herrington
Houghton-Le-Spring Tyne & Wear,
DH4 7AA, UK

British Library Cataloguing-in-Publication Data.
A Catalogue record for this book is available
from the British Library.

ISBN: 978-0-9543268-1-4

Cover design photographs
Phill Dougan, 2007
www.Phillip Dougan.com

Printed and bound by Athenaeum Press Ltd,
Gateshead, Tyne & Wear, England

This book is dedicated
to our late granddaughter
NIKI
Who died on the 9th of February 2001
at the tender age of sixteen
to cystic fibrosis.

ACKNOWLEDGEMENTS

To Ronnie Potter neighbour and good friend, for
his patience assisting me in the preparation of this
book. Without his help this book would still be an
uncorrected manuscript.

To Michael Marwood, Geoffery Postill & our Granddaughters
Chelsea and Jamie Leigh Liddle, for all their help in the
technical preparation of this book.(i.e) the computer.

LETTER OF THANKS

From sister Revell and the staff of the cystic fibroses ward at St James hospital Leeds.

Thank you for the continued donations sent over the past few years from the sale of your book *RICH WITHOUT MONEY.*

The staff and myself wish Mr and Mrs Liddle every success with their new book *THE CRAZIEST GAMBLE,* hoping the sales are as successful as their first book, good luck, and once again thank you.

Sister Revell

CHAPTER ONE

Several months had passed since that unforgettable night when I'd discovered the identity of both my father and my mother, it was a shock to say the least. Brought up from an early age by my grandparents. I'd never bothered asking questions as to why, or how there was no mother or father on the scene. I was simply quite happy the way things were.

My life from the age of ten had revolved around the love of greyhounds, that's what led me to work for a man called Harry Slone back in the North East of England in the early Sixties. My wife and I moved from Barnsley where an accident in the mines and an injury to my back had forced me to leave the pits and seek work a little less strenuous.

Being an ex miner injured in the mines I was lucky enough to qualify for an old pit house which eventually as sitting tenants we were offered the chance to buy. Harry Slone, my shock father had decided to move on after that eventful night.

The disgrace he had brought to the village with the beatings of his wife and the cruel treatment he'd dished out to his dogs was enough to make the man leave in shame. The hiding he'd received from me on the night it was discovered he was my father also had more than a little bearing on his leaving.

It wasn't long after this incident with Slone that my newly discovered mother died. I often wondered had it not been for that dreadful night when I learned that Slone was my father and aunt Mary was my mother, whether she might still be alive.

Jill my wife tried on several occasions to reassure me that it was not of my doing, but it was always there at the back of my mind and I knew the feeling of guilt would live with me forever.

Our lives were slowly coming back together after the toll of the last few months, the three oldest boys had made the football teams at their new schools, our biggest problem was trying to watch all three at the same time, at different football grounds, not an easy task

We had kept in touch with our friends in Ireland and were still having dogs sent over, but on occasions I still loved to make the long trip to the Emerald Isle myself. I'd fallen in love with the place, the people and everything about it, next to my wife and kids Ireland was at the top of my list.

Jill and I had started training dogs for other people with the help of Billy my best mate. This was a new venture for Jill and myself, as we had only trained dogs belonging to ourselves. We had some good owners who loved the dogs and not just the winning side of it, but there is always one bad apple in the barrel. That bad apple and his cronies will emerge in the chapters to follow and play a villainous part in both my own and Jill's life. The events that unfold will both shock and disgust you.

CHAPTER TWO

The loud banging on the door startled me as I dozed in the old rocking chair. I jumped to my feet and headed for the door to find a small boy breathless and frightened.

"It's---It's old---Jacob," he gasped. "Herman---and his men are trying tu kill him Mr Watson," the poor little mite was shaking with fear. "Who sent yer son," I asked as I slipped on my coat, but before I could get an answer the boy was nowhere to be seen.

I pulled on my old boots and shouted to Jill my wife that I wouldn't be long. It wasn't that far down to the village, but for quickness I decided to take the van. I arrived to find old Jacob, a Jewish gentleman being tended to by Mrs Bickerstaff who owned the second-hand shop two doors down from Jacob's tailors. A kindly soul she was, frail and tired looking with big bushy eyebrows and a heart as big as the old black hat that accompanied her wherever she went. Small she may have been but she feared no one.

As I looked down, blood poured from the nose of the defenceless old man as he lay there on the ground looking up at his flamed filled shop. This was the work of an evil piece of scum, his name was Paul Chapman, or Herman the German, a nickname that had attached itself to the character of this Jew hating piece of shit and a name he seemed to be proud of.

It wasn't just the Jews that Herman hated, it was anyone that wasn't white, whether they were British born or not. Not content with giving the old man a knocking about and a bloody nose, he was also trying to burn down his shop. Mrs Bickerstaff told me that Herman and his henchmen had dragged the old man by his long grey hair up and down the street in full view of the curtain twitches and cowards that hid behind their doors.

The humiliation must have been horrendous, not a soul came to the aid of the old man for fear of reprisals, except frail Mrs Bickerstaff. You could perhaps understand the reason for this. Herman the Jew hater was a man to be feared, and with good reason.

He was into protection rackets, drugs, prostitution, anything that was illegal and made money, but most of all from violence.

That's where this excuse for a man found his kicks. Jacob was the only man amongst the business people who wouldn't pay for protection, hence the treatment and humiliation he received. Unfortunately this wasn't the first time the old man had been made an example of.

For some reason this scumbag hadn't bothered Mrs Bickerstaff's second-hand shop, perhaps that was because of the old lady's friendship with Herman's late mother. I on the other hand had only crossed paths with this parasite at the dog track, but always from a healthy spitting distance.

No conversation or pleasantries and that's just the way I wanted it, knowing of his reputation for violence. At 5ft 8ins and about ten and a half stone, I was no John Wayne. But if it came to the crunch I'd stand my ground with anyone who threatened me, or my family.

I picked up the old man and placed him in the van, he weighed no more than seven or eight stone wet through. Curtains twitched, the doors slightly ajar. We were being watched by the cowards that had stood by and seen a defenceless old man take a beating from someone who couldn't hold a light to this man's character. "You spineless bastards," I yelled at the top of my voice as I wiped the blood from my hands before closing the van door and setting off for home. I pulled up gently outside my little terraced house taking care not to inflict more pain on the old man. Jill my wife, held open the door as I carried old Jacob into the passage smudging the wall with blood from his clothes. "My god Tom, what the hells happened." "No time tu explain Jill, call Doctor Carroll," I said as I lay the old man on the settee.

"No Doctor----my dear," whispered the old man, his voice very weak.

"Jacob you need a Doctor." "No doctor---Tom," he repeated.

"If I go to hospital---that Herman will think he has won---it will take more than someone like him to drive me from my shop," the old gent paused to catch his breath while struggling to try to lift himself up from the settee. "When,"--- he gasped, his voice very low. "When I was in the concentration camp---- you could not show weakness--- or you would not live to see the next day," the old man stopped to take in a deep breath then continued. "I had to endure more pain than what that excuse for a human being could do to me, things that would make even that coward wince."

The old man once again tried to ease himself up from the settee, blood still rolling down his face into his grey beard from a gash on the bridge of his nose. Jill hurried in from the kitchen with a bowl of hot water and a handful of bandages.

Jacob had three or four cuts to his head and hands that didn't seem to be too bad. Tearfully Jill wiped away the blood from the old man's wounds, his hair entangled with a mixture of blood and dirt from the street, the biggest problem was his nose, no matter what we did we couldn't stop the bleeding.

"I'm afraid your nose looks as if it's broken Jacob," I said holding his nose with an old towel we used for the dogs.

"With----a nose like mine Tom--- he gasped, what could you expect my dear." The old man might have been in some pain but he still had his dry sense of humour.

We cleaned up old Jacob the best way we could, gave him a cup of tea, his favourite drink and begged him to stay the night.

He was having none of it, he struggled to his unsteady feet, stood up as straight as he possibly could holding onto the arm of a chair, he looked me straight in the eye and said in a whispered voice.

"Tom -----would you let a piece of scum like that----that, I can't find the words to say---in front of your good lady, it would not be right." I looked at the old man, blood still running down from his nose. "I understand what you are trying to say Jacob and I'd probably do the same as you, but what about your shop and your flat, it must be in a right mess?"

"To-night Tom--- I sleep under the stars if I have to, I will not let that piece of shit, excuse me my language good lady," said Jacob bowing his head and apologizing at the same time,

"But I will not be driven from my home, I will not," he shook his head in sheer frustration and anger. It was obvious old Jacob was not going to change his mind no matter how much we tried to convince him that staying would be the best thing to do, his mind was made up.

I helped him outside and into the van. We drove slowly

6

down to his little shop in the village. The place was deadly silent, no sign of the fire engine and not knowing if the police had even been there? I asked Jacob to wait in the van until I'd checked the extent of the damage. I hadn't gone through the charred door before he was right behind me. The familiar smell of damp burned wood hung in the air, fortunately the damage looked to be in the lower part of the premises. Herman and his crew seemed to be more intent on humiliating old Jacob as a warning to the others, rather than burning it down.

We ventured upstairs to find very little damage, mostly from the heavy smoke. Jacob eased his way over to an old tin box on a shelf, I thought to myself this must be the old man's savings, he hovered over the box, nervously trying to take off the lid, pain etched on his face as he struggled to open the it.

Tears welling up in his eyes with anxiety and frustration wondering if the box would still have its contents. The lid came off and fell to the floor, he had an expression on his face that I didn't know which way to take.

The old man looked at me with a trance like glare, a trickle of blood running down from his nose as he stared back into the box, a half smile came over Jacob's wrinkled and bloodied face, a few missing teeth evidence of the lack of calcium in his diet from his days in the concentration camp when he was a boy. "Tom--- my boy," said the old man, his eyes still full.

"These are my most valuable possessions." I ventured forward and glanced into the soot-covered tin, its contents were old photographs.

Jacob looked at me with tear filled eyes. It was clear the ordeal with Herman and the contents of the box had made the old man quite emotional as he took a deep breath.

"The contents of this box Tom my boy, is worth more than all the money in the world to me--- it is irreplaceable." He took an old piece of rag from his pocket, wiped his eyes and bloodied nose, composed himself and then continued to speak, pausing every few seconds.

"My mamma----my papa---my sister and brothers, cousins, aunts and uncles," the old man hesitated and reached out to support himself on the arm of an old chair. It was all too much for him as he collapsed into the chair, the tin box falling to the floor.

His clenched hand holding onto its contents, a few pictures with the memories he cherished of his loved ones.

"All gone Tom---all gone---I feel guilty that I should have survived, that I am alive to tell of my kinfolk killed by the likes of scum like Herman," the old mans head slumped forward, his hands clenching the photographs close to his heart. Jacob broke down and wept uncontrollably. It was time for me to depart. I said my goodbyes, but to be honest, I think my words went straight over the old mans head, it was obvious his thoughts were elsewhere.

I closed what was left of the downstairs door and made my way home, I too had become overwhelmed with the old mans story and wondered to myself how human beings could be so cruel and evil to one another.

After attending to the dogs the following day I made my way down to the village to check on Jacob, I was amazed to see the old man in the thick of it, as if nothing had happened.

I stood there looking in total admiration at a man who had been through hell and back the night before, to see him up on his feet and working.

The resilience to stand up to the likes of Herman and his

cronies showed his backbone to the rest of the community. Jacob was in the doorway throwing out some burnt material when he caught sight of me.

"Tom my boy, I can't thank you and Jill enough for all your help last night, I could maybe have died, maybe," his hands clutching mine, his face visible of the cuts and bruises he'd received from his beating.

"We will get even with this Herman German one day Tom, you wait and see, we will beat him with the brains, not the brawn, like we did in the camp, no time for talking Tom my boy, must get on with my work my neighbours they have businesses to run." Jacob carried on with his work singing softly to himself in what I presumed was Jewish. How he could turn his back on the previous night as if nothing had happened I would never understand.

The old man and I knew that Herman would raise his ugly head again; a chill ran down my spine just with the thought of what he could and might do in the future.

I had a gut feeling that Herman would not be on the scene for some time, he had a habit of disappearing for a while after one of his little escapades like this, it was most likely advice from his paid police friends to keep his head low for the time being. If my hunch was right, this would at least give me a little breathing space and time to work out a plan of revenge for this man who I knew would be thinking of some evil and hurtful way to harm me and my family, all because I'd given help to an old Jewish man who just wanted to get on with his life. Little did I know at that time that myself and my family and friends were to have more than one bad encounter with Herman in the future. My marriage, house and kids would all be under threat.

CHAPTER THREE

Billy, my best mate and I were walking along the river bank with the greyhounds. It was one of those days when you could smell the foliage of the trees and the scent of the flowers after a good downpour of rain. We had two dogs each, one black, Sooty, two fawn, Pat and Mick, plus the old brindle dog Ben, he was knocking on in years was old Ben, but still as lively as the rest of them. His days of racing were over due to an injury he'd sustained on the track.

Suddenly Ben started pulling on his lead in the direction of some freshly dug earth just above the path. "Must be something in there Tom for the old rascal to act the way he is," said Billy, who stood just over six feet tall his arms full of tattoos bulging with the strain of the dogs pulling on their leads.

We were being pulled towards what I took to be a large molehill just off the path to the forest side of the river. Ben pricked up his ears and started pulling harder towards the mound of earth.

"Must be something in there Billy, must be," I said trying to keep my feet from slipping on the wet ground, the old dog nearly pulling my arms from their sockets.

We were nearly on top of the mound, when I thought I heard a very faint squeak, I stood still and listened for few seconds.

"Hold tight onto those dogs Billy, it might be a mole, but ah don't think it is because I've never heard a mole squeak

10

when down in the hole."

I stood motionless with my head cocked to one side, not a sound apart from the birds singing.

"If it's a mole these dogs will kill the poor little mite and I think he'll have enough enemies without us adding to his foe." Billy managed to tie his dogs to a tree. I was still having trouble with the old dog Ben, as I slipped on the greasy surface falling onto my knees. I handed the old dog to Billy and tied Sooty to a tree then I knelt over the mound of earth--- all was quiet, we listened for a few seconds more. I stood up, wiped the sludge from my clothes, untied the dogs and set off walking. The old dog stopped dead turned and pulled back towards the mound of earth. "Must be something in there Tom, for the old lad tu act the way he is."

"Yer right Billy- there's only one way to find out," once again I tied the dogs to a tree and started to dig with my hands.

The soil was soft, freshly dug and easy to manage, I'd only gone down about a foot to eighteen inches when I pulled my hand away quickly,

"What's up, laughed Billy, it's not a snake is it," he asked creasing up with laughter. "Whatever it is Bill, it's wet and slimy."

I started to dig a bit deeper …this time with a little more caution, I cleared the soil from around the edge to examine the contents of the hole and discovered it was some sort of sack.

I pulled the sack from the hole and held it out at arms length not knowing what to expect. It was tied with a piece of baling twine at the top; I was a bit dubious as what to do next. Whatever it was, it wasn't light.

11

"Go on then Tom, open it up," said Billy, a large smirk on his face. "It won't bite or will it?"

I laid the bag on the ground and started to untie the twine with caution, there wasn't a sound to be heard. I gently emptied out the contents onto the grass--- and to my horror and disgust it contained four pups, all motionless, three fawns and one black.

On closer examination I was sure that they looked like greyhound pups. Billy and I stood there, speechless, just shaking our heads in sheer disbelief, whoever did this despicable thing had to be the lowest piece of scum on the earth. I placed the pups back into the sack to make their final resting place a bit more discreet.

The hole looked like it had been dug in a hurry, I made it bigger and deeper than when we'd found it to try and keep out the predators, I lifted the sack to place it back into the hole, when Ben let off an almighty howl.

I was startled so much that I dropped the bag into the hole, then a faint sound from the sack took my attention.

I grabbed the sack and gently picked out each pup, there was no sign of life in the first three, as I picked out the last pup, a black dog, he suddenly sneezed, my face was covered in mucous. I quickly cleaned his nose and blew into his mouth, a few more coughs and splutters and you could see the little fellow was fighting for his life.

I ran down to the riverside, gave him a quick dip or two to remove the rest of the dirt from his head and body, to my joy the little rascal responded with a shake from the shock of the cold water.

Billy and I hurriedly checked the rest of the litter for any sign of life, but alas there was none. We quickly buried the remaining pups and set off home as quickly as our legs would carry us, the survivor showing a bit more life as he wriggled inside my jumper.

We arrived at the kennels, placed the big dogs into the paddocks and gave our full attention to the pup, he wasn't underfed, neither were the other pups and I started to wonder why? Why try to kill four healthy pups? I stood there scratching my head, but for the life of me, I couldn't understand the evilness of this so-called human being who could stoop as low as to do this.

A thought came into my head that this could be the work of that evil bastard Herman.

Shit I thought, I must be getting paranoid after what had happened to Jacob. *Come on Tom, give yer head a shake I said to myself.*

I'd guessed the pup's age at about eight to ten weeks, with no earmarks for identification. Despite this little pup's ordeal he seemed to be in good health, why, or how, this little fellow had survived when the others hadn't was something we will never know.

From what Billy and I could make out of this terrible situation, some evil bastard had tried to drown these pups for some sick reason and probably been disturbed by kids swimming in the river, or someone walking their dog, panicked, then hurriedly tried to bury them. *I just couldn't shake Herman from my head.*

About twelve months had passed since we rescued that little black pup and he'd turned out to be a fine looking animal, despite his cruel start to life.

We had decided to call him Lucky, for obvious reasons. He was just the right size for the flapping tracks (Independent

13

dog racing tracks) weighing about 70 pounds and looked every inch a greyhound, we had estimated his age now at about 14 to 15 months and just right for schooling. We had made lots of enquires about the circumstances of that eventful day when we found that shallow grave along the side of the riverbank, but all to no avail.

There was one name that cropped up on more than one occasion, our old friend Herman the German, who fortunately hadn't been seen for some considerable time. Rumours were strong that he'd been caught doing a job on someone else's patch and had fled down south to London for his own safety. It was inevitable that he would raise his ugly head again, as his cronies had continued with his evil racketeering.

CHAPTER FOUR

Six months later, still no word of Herman, perhaps the rumours were true that he'd fled down south, I was prepared to take the risk and go to the Sales in Ireland, knowing that Billy and the lads were there for Jill and the kids.

It was a rough old journey in that old bone shaker of a van from the North East of England to the Emerald Isle but well worth the trouble, I adored the people and the place.

I'd been back in England about a week putting the new dogs I'd bought through their paces up the gallop, when an owner of a couple of dogs I had in training for him came to see me at the kennels.

Harry Homes was his name, a short stout man with a boozer's nose and villain wrote all over his face. Everyone called him Mr H, or H, for short, but to be honest, the names I used and many others can't be repeated.

He passed himself off as a millionaire and he may have been at one time, now it took him all his time to pay his kennel bill--- and anyone else that he owed money too. Harry owed quite a few people besides me, but if I gave him his marching orders with his two dogs, I dreaded to think where the dogs might end up? The welfare of the dogs was my main concern.

The two dogs Mr H, owned, were decent dogs and he knew if he didn't pay the kennel bill, the dogs eventually would be mine.

"Nice dogs there, Tom," said H, casting a glance at the

new arrivals, not that he'd know which end of a dog to feed.

"Yes they don't look a bad lot H, with a little luck there may be one or two handy animals amongst them," I replied. Not that I would tell that little fat toad if there was anything handy or otherwise. I had to keep sweet with him just in case there was a slight chance of being paid the kennel bill.

H, continued asking questions, like how much did the dogs cost and which one was the best dog amongst them, I pointed to a good looking black dog with one half white leg.

"Flying machine that feller H, money can't buy that dog, he belongs to a chap who wants him for top class open racing." H stood there as if in a trance his beady little eyes fixed on the dog in question.

"That good is he Tom," said H, rubbing his grubby little fingers up and down his chin, a mischievous look on that villains face that spelt trouble.

Little did H know, that the dog in question couldn't run a message, never mind win a race. The owner had sent him over to be given to a good home rather than being put to sleep. After his inquisitive questions, H turned on his heels and proceeded to leave the kennels.

"Hold on there, H, what about paying off some of that kennel bill you owe," I shouted as his stride lengthened as he scurried off up the path.

"Next week Tom, when my bitch is on the card, next week," he repeated as he scrambled through the gate, and you could bet your life you wouldn't see hide nor hair of him until race day. I was just curious as to why he was asking all the questions about the dogs?

Jill, my wife, was as passionate about the dogs as I was and did just as much work, even with four kids to look after, the youngest being Paul.

We had seven dogs in racing, but I have to admit Spotty, a fawn bitch with white specks on her ears was our favourite, with a special love for Lucky, the pup we had saved from a certain death.

Spotty had been sent over by a friend of ours in Ireland for a syndicate of bookmakers, she was as dodgy as a cuckoo, but she dodged the right way, two lengths in front, no more, no less.

We never knew how fast she was because she never extended herself and that was just the way I liked her, the handicapper couldn't grade her because he didn't know how fast she was, and the punters never knew if she was going to stop and dodge, or go on about her work, but I always had total faith in her when the money was down.

I was just about to leave the kennels when Jimmy an old friend of mine and his son popped in to see me, Jimmy the beard as he was known for obvious reasons.

Terry was his son's name, always dressed immaculate, his manners impeccable, and an all-round nice lad. But Terry had a problem. He had learning difficulties, not that you would notice too much, because Terry had talents you would kill for.

Jimmy explained to me that Terry never spoke a word until he was seven years old; the first word he spoke was Russian (despradanya) meaning (goodbye) he was an avid telly watcher as a small child and must have picked up the word from the T.V. From then on he never stopped talking.

Jimmy told me about the day his daughter Allison, asked Terry a question.

"Terry," she asked, "Why didn't you speak until you were seven years old." To Terry the answer was simple. "*I had nothing to say."* Apparently his daughter sat there gob smacked with the answer her brother had given her. Terry sat watching the telly as if the answer was as normal as day and night.

Terry also had a photographic memory, he only had to see an object once and he could draw whatever it might be right down to the last detail, all from memory, he was the same with birthdays numbers and dates.

But his love of sixties and seventies rock and roll music was out of this world, he could tell you what was top at any time of that era, how long they had stayed there for and how many records the artist or artists had sold. Terry was amazing, after trying to catch him out on several different questions for fifteen minutes I gave up, "Call it a day, Terry, I'll think of something for the next time we meet."

That was something else about Terry, he never forgot, you could bet money on the next time we'd meet it could be six months, or six years, Terry would ask for the question, a remarkable young man.

Saturday night, we were racing at Ships End Track, it was called that because of all the ships that went to the scrap yard a few hundred yards from the track.

We pulled into the car park, Lady knew she was at the track and stood up wagging her tail. Jill watched the kids out of the van while I held onto Lady. Ray Foster and Billy were already there sitting in Billy's car. The pair looked quite comical sitting in that little old car of his with their knees up to their chins. Ray stood about six foot five and Billy over six feet tall.

I had informed them both earlier that we might have a bit of business on. Both Billy and Ray knew better than to ask what the business was until we were all together at the track, then we could discuss the details of how much was being bet and to what bookmakers we were going to bet with.

After walking Lady around for a few minutes to make sure she was emptied, I booked her in at the kennels while Jill ushered the kids under the turnstile. The dog we were running belonged to H, a nice little brindle bitch called House Warmer, the name came from H, because that used to be his business, building and selling houses. *And robbing people.*

The bitch had a real good chance, Billy, Ray and myself intended to have a good bet on (Lady) her pet name, that's if we could avoid H and tell him just before the race that his bitch was busy.

H had the biggest mouth in the North East and would tell everyone and their mother that the bitch was trying. More importantly, he couldn't be trusted. We were doing a good job avoiding H, with only two races to go before Lady's race, I'd gone to the bar for some crisps for the kids, Jill was to follow me in, collect the crisps and leave.

I stood behind a big pillar in the bar. I thought this would be the last place H would look, with me being a non-drinker.

I was wrong, Jill had left the kids with Billy and Ray and then walked towards the bar unawares that little Paul our youngest had run after her. H, who must have been watching Jill like a hawk, followed Paul and grabbed his hand. I had just given the crisps to Jill, when H, popped his head around the pillar.

"This little lad yours, Tom," he smirked. "It's just I thought he might be lost ---and we wouldn't want that---- would we," he said with a wicked look in his eyes. H was in with all the wrong people, Herman being one of them. I also didn't like his tone of voice, to be honest I wouldn't put anything past that evil little man. Jill took hold of Paul's hand.

"He's not lost and never has been," growled Jill, there was no one fiercer when it came to protecting her kids, she was like a lioness with her cubs.

Off Jill marched, dragging little Paul behind her, his ten steps to Jill's two, his little legs finding it difficult to keep up.

"Right Tom, lets get down to business," said H, rubbing his hands like the miser he was.

I was in a corner now, I had no choice but to tell him the dog was busy. The bitch had been held up the last three times she had run, well galloped before running her race at the track to make sure she was not at her best.

"What price do you think she's going to be Tom," asked H, an evil look in his beady little eyes. "Three to one, four to one, something like that," I replied. "Now the big question Tom, will she win," he asked, his eyes never leaving mine, looking for any telltale sign that I may not be telling him the truth.

"She has a good shout if she breaks well from the traps, but you know this game H, anything can happen." *I didn't want to sound too confident.*

"You'll do for me Tom," he said pushing his hand deep into his pocket. *I knew the bitch had a right good chance, but I also knew H, would want a fortune on.* I was prepared for the worst when he pulled his hand from his pocket.

"There you are Tom, get me £30 on." I looked at H in amazement. "£30 that's not your normal bet H, things aren't that bad are they?" H looked a bit shifty rubbing his chin and shuffling his feet, I smelt a rat. "Er---that's it Tom, every penny I've got, I don't know what I'll do if this dog gets

20

beat," he replied---I had a gut feeling that something was wrong, very wrong.

We were soon to find out, Lady was in the next race. I asked Billy to parade her instead of Jill, especially as Mr H was only having £30 on. There was also another reason why I had asked Billy.

Jill wasn't too pleased at being relieved of the job of leading Lady onto the track---she was also wise enough to know not to ask questions and that there had to be a reason for the change of plan.

Ray and myself walked down towards the bookmakers, we were amazed at the price, even money favourite.

There was only one explanation, someone had backed Lady before the race and we had a good idea who.

A bookmaker's clerk to whom Mr H owed money informed me that H had bet £500 before the race at 3-1. This left Billy, Ray and myself with even money ---*what a pity I thought to myself...* H was in for a shock. "THE DOGS INTO THE TRAPS MR STARTER," came the announcement.

Under instruction, Billy had not taken his eyes off me, I'd given him a prearranged signal which he acknowledged and the business was done, nobody the wiser. Up went the traps, all the dogs came out pretty level, it was a 500yd race. With only 200yds to go. Lady was disputing the lead when she started to drop back, eventually finishing fourth and limping off the track.

H, came storming round to the paddock, "How the hell did that bitch get beat," he screamed. "She's gone lame H, look at her, even you can see her limping," I replied. Lady was standing on three legs holding up her front left paw.

"But the good thing is H, you didn't lose your money, we

didn't bet her with the odds being so short----so you still have your £30 and everyone is happy--- *that is except the people that had backed her before the race."* You could see the anger in his face boiling up as if it were ready to burst. He knew that we knew he'd backed Lady before the race. He also knew that we had prevented the bitch from winning--- but what he didn't know, was *how!*

H, stormed off cursing and blinding like a man looking for revenge and we knew he would do his utmost to achieve it.

We walked off towards the car park, the bitch still limping for all to see. Billy picked her up and carried her to the van.

"Nice one Billy, make it look authentic." He carefully lifted the bitch into the back of the van, then I proceeded to examine her foot for all to see. I started the van and left the track out of sight of any prying eyes.

"Right Bill," I winked. "You can take that elastic band off her foot now." It was a trick I had used on many occasions, especially when someone had stolen the betting market. My philosophy was, if my money wasn't on--- *NOBODY WAS ON*. The bitch wasn't harmed in any way. My only concern was, what would be the next move by Mr Harry Homes?

The next couple of weeks passed without incident, still no sign of Mr H. It felt very eerie, you had a feeling something was going to happen---but you didn't know what, where, or when. We decided to get on with things the best way we could, keeping an extra eye on the kids, keeping them as near to home as possible. No one was pleased about it especially the kids, but they knew we had no choice and like little troopers they took it on the chin.

We had entered Spotty in a race at Downhill Track, a nice family run track with a good atmosphere. Mr and Mrs Ryan owned the track, an Irish couple that had eight kids and didn't seem to have a care in the world----apart from wanting to kill each other at one time or another.

Spotty had a great chance, giving a staggered start of up to 7 yards to the dog off the front, that was just the way she liked it, something to chase, the only problem was the price, it would be very short, even money 5-4 at best. The race read like this.

1 Red Jacket. Spotty scratch
2 Blue ------ Snowball 2 yards
3 white------ Happy Jack 4 yards
4 black ----- Smokey 6 yards
5 orange----- Minnie 6 yards
6 stripes blk-whi-----Salty 7 yards

All the lads from the syndicate who owned Spotty were there, including the big boss, Phill, who owned about thirty betting shops and definitely wasn't short of a bob or two and loved the thrill of having a bet on his own dogs and beating his fellow bookmakers at the same time.

"What chance has she got," asked Martin, the main spokesman for the group, a tall thin man with glasses as thick as milk bottle bottoms. "I can't see her getting beat Martin," I replied.

"But the price will be short and there's not much we can do about that I'm afraid." Martin about turned and headed off in the direction of the rest of the syndicate, speaking to everyone and anyone on his way.

The Ryan's were at each other's throats once again. You could here them screaming at one another in the judge's box and believe me the language was choice, little did they realize the mike was still on.

It was only when Patrick one of the Ryan's kids, who was also the hare driver caught their attention, did they stop.

"Take no notice of dat little discussion wit der wife lady's and gentlemen," said Mr Ryan in his smooth Irish voice. "Tis just a disagreement wit me and the misses, I love her to pieces-- so I do and dat might be what she'll end up in when we get home so she will," laughed Mr Ryan. Mrs Ryan giving him a look that could scare a banshee.

"Over my dead body yer old goat," shouted his wife, never one to back down. The mike still on for everyone to hear.

"I'm looking forward tu the day when I'm dancing on yer grave so I am yer, yer old goat dat yer are," she screamed at her husband.

"And I'm looking forward tu the day dat you will be dancing on me grave so I am... Molley Ryan ... for I've left strict instructions tu be buried at SEA, so what du yer tin'k of dat, Misses."

"You'll regret dat Shamus Ryan so yer will tu yer dying day--- *dat's if yer live dat long,* " she replied. There was never a dull moment with the old Irish couple and I often thought that most of the public only came to the track for a laugh and they weren't often disappointed.

The Ryan's sorted out their differences and got on with the meeting as though nothing had happened.

The announcement was made for the next race, the third.

Everything went off as normal, as if there hadn't been a wrong word said between the Ryan's.

We were in the fourth race. Jill had the job of parading Spotty, taking the kids with her, all in Indian file; the bitch was used to the kids and didn't seem to mind the attention. The Ryan's didn't worry about the kids being on the track as

24

long as they stood in the middle and behaved themselves; after all, they had eight kids of their own and were quite understanding.

Phill the boss, a smartly dressed man, with a little red birthmark on his on his cheekbone came over to ask me about the race. "Tom, if Spotty wasn't in this race what would you have a bet on," he asked. "That's a funny thing to ask Phill, but you must have a good reason." "I have Tom," he said. "Well in that case Salty would be my choice Phill, but there's not a cat in hell's chance of Salty beating the bitch."

"No problem Tom, just wanted to see what the danger was," he said as he walked off in the direction of the other lads.

Phill and the rest of the syndicate were doing the betting, the lads loved to be in on the action mixing it with their opposition bookmakers. Spotty opened up even money favourite, that's just about what I expected, but what I didn't expect, was Phill to go down the line betting Salty at every board, I could see his price slashed from 2/1 to evens favourite. The bookies and the punters must have thought that our dog Spotty wasn't busy. (A saying in the racing world for a dog or horse not doing it's best).

There were six bookies and from what I could see, Phill had bet £100 on each one of them, by now the boss had me scratching my head and the worst of it was he had our money to bet on Spotty!

"One minute to the off," came the announcement. What the hell was going on I asked myself! Spotty's price had gone from even money to 3/1. I was just about to have a bet myself on the bitch, when Phill, Martin and the rest of the team steamed into the books once again. When the dust had cleared and the confusion over, there was no price left for Spotty.

No time to find out what was what, the race was on it's way and as predicted Spotty was making her way to the front of the pack weaving in and out of the other dogs like a snake. It was hard to tell who was running the hardest, the kids on the inner circle of the track, or the dogs chasing the hare.

Spotty won the race by her usual two lengths, once she led something dreadful would have to happen for her to be beaten and that didn't bear thinking about.

First number one Spotty, second trap six Salty, der winner won by two lengths.

It wasn't hard to work out what Phill had done when we saw him collecting from all the bookies, he had laid out £600 on Salty at 2-1 to create a false favourite, the dog did have a slight chance of winning, but in my opinion Spotty would have had to fall down for him to win the race.

What Phill was doing wasn't illegal; he was hedging his bets, because he also had £600 on Spotty at 3-1, should Salty win, Phill draws £1200.

If Spotty wins, he draws £1800, take the £600 from Spotty's winnings to pay the bookies for his losing bet and you end up £1200 in front, not my way of betting, mainly because of the lack of funds.

Phill was a percentage man, the way he looked at it, this was the best way to win on a race, a millionaire with about thirty betting shops, or me with one brown lace in one shoe and a black in the other, it wasn't hard to work out who was right!

Martin came over with our winnings; he was like a big kid who had just got his first bike. He couldn't contain himself as he handed over the winnings with a big smile.

"There you are Tom, 3-1 for all your cash," he said, slapping the money into my hand, a grin from ear to ear.

He started to walk off then stopped in his tracks. "Nearly forgot Tom, the boss said job well done and sorry if he got you confused, but you know what he's like, if he can get one over on the other books he's in his element, you know it isn't the money, it's the thrill of beating the opposition." Off Martin walked head held high then nearly tripping over his size eleven feet as he went.

We counted out the winnings to odds of three to one. A cracking price for a bitch that should have been even money at the best, but that wasn't the end of it; there was £100 over the top. I shouted out to Martin as he and the lads headed for the bar.

"Martin, there's £100 to much, you must have made a mistake." "No mistake Tom, that's from the boss," he said laughing to himself. "Phill said you had to buy a new pair of laces."

Billy, the kids, Jill and Ray all looked down at my shoes together and burst out laughing, that is all but Jill.

"First thing in the morning Tom Watson," she said, "You are up tu them shops for a new pair of laces, I'm not having people taking pity thinking we can't afford a pair of bloody laces." "Jill, sweetheart," I replied, "If someone wants to give me £100 for a pair of laces next time I'm going to blacken my feet with boot polish, then lace up my toe's and see what that brings!" Jill went silent; she gave me one of her don't know which way to take looks, then glanced at the kids and burst out laughing.

"You great idiot, you'll have the kids believing you about the polish." "I wasn't kidding!" I said as we walked out of the track, a cheeky grin on my face and a half smile half frown on Jill's.

We headed off home with our usual routine of calling at the fish and chip shop. Mrs Moffit owned the shop and had done ever since I can remember from being a small boy. A real nice lady, but she had one of the worst stutters I have ever heard, she had never changed over all the years I'd known her. No matter when you told her to stop with the salt--- it was always too late, even the kids knew what to expect.

They would all stand in a line ready for the shaking of the salt and try to stop her putting too much on the fish and chip lots. There she would stand, salt seller in one hand, the chips in the other--- "DDo you want aaanyy sssssssaaaalllt on TTTTOM, then the kids would all shout in harmony, plenty on Mrs Moffit, plenty on! But it was always too late, the more she stuttered, the more salt went on the chips, you could see the kids looking at each other and shaking their heads a lot slower than Mrs Moffit did with that salt seller.

CHAPTER FIVE

Weeks had gone by without incident, no sighting of Mr H, or Herman anywhere, his dogs were still in our care and the kennel bill was mounting, not that I was worried, I'd rather have the dogs than the bill, at least we knew where they were.

We started to relax a little, giving the kids more freedom. Christmas was just around the corner and the kids would want to join their mates carol singing.

Christmas time was always hard for Jill and I, four kids to buy for and money very scarce. But for the past couple of years we had an ace up our sleeve with Spotty, you would just think she knew when the chips were down and if entered for a race, she would always come up trumps.

Four weeks before Christmas, the kids were writing out their lists of what they would like, and getting excited at the thought of what they might get.

Our kennels were about half a mile from our house and a real chew in the winter. Snow had fallen through the night and the roads were bad, it took a little longer that morning to reach the kennels, as usual the council had been caught out and the roads were worse than we expected.

As we drove up the drive skidding from side to side, I sensed something was wrong! There were other tracks partly covered by the snow.

As we approached the gate each morning the dogs would recognize the sound of the van and start barking, this morning the sound was minimal. Jill, the kids and I, all looked at each other without saying a word. We scrambled out of the van making our way towards the gate ----the lock had been broken as had the lock to the kennels. The reality of the situation soon became apparent when we found four of the kennel doors wide open.

Spotty's and the two dogs belonging to Mr H, plus the kennel belonging to the dog with the white leg, which I had told H, was an open race dog. Jill had taken a fancy to him and decided to keep him as a pet.

This had to be the work of that no good lousy low life H; it was bad enough taking his own dogs to avoid paying his kennel bill, but to take Spotty and the other dog was below the belt. Jill half-heartedly, said, "It may not be him Tom, it could be someone else."

In a way Jill was right, H wouldn't have the bottle to try this on his own. He'd have paid someone else to do his dirty work.

We fed the dogs that were left and gave them a little exercise then drove home. I kept saying to myself, why Spotty? In the end it didn't take a lot of working out, she was the best dog in the kennel. If there was a small consolation, whoever took the dogs, didn't take Lucky the black pup. We informed the police of the break in and gave a description of the dogs along with their earmarks, but I held very little hope of them ever being found again.

If it was H and his cronies, it didn't bear thinking about what they might do to Spotty; a cold shiver ran down my spine just at the thought.

If my train of thinking was right, this low life would stop at nothing to seek his revenge.

It was in my mind that Herman was involved in all this

somewhere along the line. If so he would stick out like a sore thumb on any dog track. At six feet four, a very distinctive scar like an arrowhead on the left side of his face, with a swastika tattooed on the back of each hand.

Herman had often done dirty work for H in the past and was often seen in his company. This excuse for a human would stop at nothing to make a few pounds and his name had cropped up more than once when we had made enquiries about the pups found near the riverbank. If he had stolen the dogs I could only fear the worst.

I phoned Martin to inform him of the situation, he was more disappointed for Jill and the kids than anything else, he knew how much Spotty meant to us all.

We posted leaflets in all the local shops, placed an advert in the local paper and informed other flapping tracks up and down the country offering a £200 reward put up by Phill, the owner of the betting shops, and to be honest, the owner of Spotty.

Christmas came and went, it was the worst time of our lives not knowing where Spotty was. With such a large reward the phone never stopped ringing, mostly time wasters, but we had to follow up each and every call. I knew in my heart that if Spotty were to be found, it would not be in our local area that would be too obvious.

We were sitting by the open fire one night, both looking like we were about to be hanged, when the phone rang and startled us. "I'll get it Jill, probably just another false alarm."

The voice on the other end of the phone had a familiar Yorkshire accent, "Is that Mr Watson." "Yes," I replied.

"This is handicapper of Donny track, it's about one of those dogs thar's looking for." My heart skipped a beat, which one was it I asked myself? The voice continued, "Ah dun't want thee tu get thee sen built up too much son, but a dog ran at track last week and there's something odd about it's ear marks."

I was glad and sad at the same time. "Did you say a dog," I asked. "That's reet lad, grand looking thing from what ah remember." My heart was hoping he was going to say a bitch.

"Where's the dog now er Mr." "Oh my names Green, but thar can call me Sam." "Right Sam, what makes you think that's it's one of our dogs!" "Ear marks have been altered and not a good job either, dog ran last week, but by time we'd realised it could be one of the stolen dogs, kid had gone." I was just about to give him a blast for letting the culprit escape, when he continued.

"Dun't worry lad, he'll be back this week, av'e put im in a race where he can't get beat, greed will me'k this chap come back son, greed," he repeated. "Thee mark my words." Listening to the old man's accent made me think briefly of the good times we had back in Yorkshire while working in the pits. "Race cards med out for Thursday son, mek sure thar's there." Before I could thank him, he'd put the phone down.

This could be it, the best lead we'd had, Jill was sitting there crying chewing on her handkerchief, we flung our arms around one another in a tight embrace. I have to admit I also had a tear in my eye. It didn't look good for Spotty, with the old man saying it was a dog, but it might lead us to her whereabouts.

I informed Martin and co just in case it was the bitch, then rang Mick, a policeman mate of mine in Yorkshire, who was also keen on the dogs. If this was Herman's doing, I was going to need the help of more than just mates, Mick was the man to handle it.

This was now a police matter. I knew Mick from way back in the dog game and if anything got up his nose more than your everyday criminal, it was the villains who corrupted the dog game with their stealing of other people's greyhounds and then when they'd used and abused them, they would discard or even shoot them, then bury the evidence. I asked Mick to bring along a couple of mates just in case things got a bit rough, I was assured that this would be taken care of.

We didn't tell the kids what was going on, just in case things went wrong at the track. Thursday morning, we were making arrangements for someone to look after the kids when the phone rang. It was Mick, he'd been onto the track at Donny and had spoken to the Handicapper, the dog was called Minty and running in the 9-15 race, giving us plenty of time to get to the track.

Mick had given the Handicapper instructions to let the dog pass the identity parade and take part in the race, reason being if we moved in to early, we would only have the chance of one arrest, the handler.

The plan was to see where the dog handler went after the race. Mick had done his homework well, with a bit of luck the handler would make straight for the rest of the gang to share out their ill-gotten gains.

We met Mick at a prearranged meeting place and proceeded to the track, it was pitch black in the car park, a good night for the job ahead. Mick decided to jump in the van with Jill and myself, his two mates in an ordinary plain car next to us, both with their uniforms covered by overcoats. The size of these lads frightened me--- and I was on their side.

We were sitting chatting for an hour or so when someone

walked past the van with a fawn bitch, he walked on for about ten yards, then stopped, looked around, then started to coat up the bitch.

"That's the bitch, that's Spotty, I'd know that walk anywhere," Jill and I always said she had a swanky walk like Marilyn Monroe, a walk you just couldn't mistake.I was just about to jump out of the van when Mick grabbed me by the coat, "Hold on Tom, just hold on," he repeated.

"If that is the bitch, and thar can't be sure from here, plus Sam Green said dog, not bitch!" Before Mick could say another word, both Jill and I were positive there was no mistake, we told Mick we knew the bitch inside out. "That's fair enough Tom, but the plan is to grab the whole gang, not just one." "He's right Tom," said Jill. "Let Mick handle the situation, we've got tu try tu keep calm.

I settled back down into my seat with a look from Jill and a little wink from Mick to assure me everything was going to plan.

"Dun't worry Tom, everything is under control, me and these lads will soon sort this out." With the window partly wound down we could hear the Handicapper call for the dogs in the 9-15 race, my heart began to pound, part of me wanted to jump out of the van to watch the race, especially now that I was convinced it was Spotty. But the sight of Mick and the size of his two mates, gave me second thoughts.

Five minutes had passed since the Handicapper had called for the dogs in the 9-15 race, it seemed like an hour, I was checking the watch every few seconds. The loudspeaker crackled into action after what seemed an age. "First number three, Minty, second number one Roman, time 28-40, distance two lengths." That was Spotty, two lengths in front. "Right

34

Tom," said Mick. "All I want thee to do is stand at the end of the paddock, when bitch passes thee and only when thar's a 100% sure---scratch your head and leave the rest tu me and my mates."

The dogs started to pass back through the paddock one by one, they'd all gone through except Spotty, my heart started thumping---. had the villains got wind and scarpered through another exit?

I was just about to leave the paddock area, when I caught sight of the handler walking up with his mates, I stood back to watch his comrades in crime draw their money from the bookies. There was no doubt that the bitch was Spotty, I just wanted to reach out and give her a big hug, but I knew that was impossible. I raised my hand to scratch my head, my eyes focused on Mick to make sure he got the signal. Mick scratched his head in acknowledgement then disappeared.

I followed the gang of three from the paddock to the car park, never taking my eyes from Spotty and her handler, then the gang stopped for a moment. I could see from where I was standing they were sharing out their winnings.

That brief moment was all that Mick and his comrades needed, they pounced in military fashion grabbing all three; Jill was on hand to grab the bitch. As the scuffle took place, a car whizzed past like a bat out of hell. I couldn't swear to it, but the driver looked like that low life Herman, a chill ran down my spine. It looked like my hunch about Herman being involved with the theft of the dogs could be right.

Mick and his mates handcuffed the three men and were trying to persuade one of them to talk. But no matter what Mick and his mates did to him, he wasn't going to co-operate in any way. It was obvious they had a bigger fear from elsewhere. If my hunch was right about Herman! The men had every reason to be afraid.

The men were placed into one of the two cars that Mick and his mates arrived in, while Jill stood with Spotty holding on tight to her lead and giving her a big hug, tears streaming down her face.

With the villains well secured, Mick and I went back into the stadium. The Handicapper was looking quite concerned, a stout little man with a red face, pacing up and down the paddock puffing on his pipe. "Er….did thar get them mate, I mean officer," he asked hurriedly, his teeth gripping onto his pipe. "All in hand Mr Green, you can relax now and get on with rest of the meeting without any worries." "Thank goodness for that," said the old gent as he puffed on his pipe like a first time father, shuffling his feet nervously. "Never mind Mr Green maybe this will help calm you down."

I counted £200 into his hand, "Ah…Ah waynt be keeping all this thar knows lad," said the old man. "Kennel staff will get their share, that's fer sure."

"That's a nice gesture Mr Green, I can't thank you enough for the recovery of the bitch." Mick and I shook his hand and said our goodbye's. The old man stuffed the money into his pocket and slapped his thigh, a smile big enough to make him nearly lose his pipe from his mouth. Mick and I couldn't help but laugh as we turned to see the old man jump into the air, click his feet together, then nearly fall over.

"What's the position now Mick," I asked, desperate to find out who was behind the theft of Spotty and the other two dogs.

"The procedure now Tom is, we get this riff- raff all three of them down tu station and get them charged."

"It should have been four, Mick, I interrupted, there was one more in the car that came flying past when the scuffle started, I'm sure he was one of the gang." "Thar's reet Tom, ah hadn't thought tu ask that scum where car, or van was that they'd travelled in, ah must be slipping up," said Mick, kicking a tin can in frustration.

"If I'm right Mick and I hope I'm not, the driver is our worst nightmare, he's a local rogue of the worst kind who would stop at nothing short of killing someone to get what he wants."

"No wonder we couldn't get a peep out of that lot, fear is a funny thing Tom, and by the smell of one of them lads, ah think fear were trying tu creep out through his trousers," said Mick with a faint smile on his face as we walked towards his mates. I think letting a little humor creep into the conversation, helped ease the tension. After all we did have Spotty back and that was a massive relief for all concerned.

I thanked Mick and his mates for their help and set off on our long journey home, at least the trip this time wasn't a wild goose chase.

Spotty was back and that made up for our dismal Christmas. Mick rang the next day to say the villains had all been charged and would appear in court at a later date. Their premises had been searched and no other dogs were found, we could only assume the worst. The three men were all staying quiet about the mysterious fourth man in the car, even denying there was a fourth man. Mick and his friends were unable to force a confession from any of the men. I was in no doubt that the fourth man was that scumbag Herman.

CHAPTER SIX

Things were starting to get back to normal, no mention of Herman from anyone, and Spotty was back to her winning ways. I'd met up with an old pal who I used to work with at the pit. Brendan Kerr, a big lad from Ireland. Brendan used to do a bit of bare knuckle fighting round the Gypsy camps, a nicer lad you couldn't wish to meet, until he was riled. Apparently he'd been working on the building sites in Germany, just the type of work that suited Brendan, lifting and carrying.

There was never a dull moment with that big Irishman around. You just had to look at him and you would burst out laughing. My last recollection of Brendan was a mop of bright ginger hair, the faintest line of hair on his top lip that was masquerading as a moustache.

His choice of clothes was out of this world. He wore the most outrageous suits and shirts that you could imagine; a green shirt with a blue jacket and red socks. You had to look at the positive side; he had very little chance of being run over.

He shook my hand vigorously until it nearly dropped off, "Nice tu see yer Tom me lad, how's Jill and the kids, how's the dogs, they tell me you've had some trouble wit some bad guys, tell me where they are Tom, just, just you just point me in der right direction I'll soon be sorting dem fellers out so I will, you leave it tu me."

"Wow Wow, Brendan, take a breath, slow down ah can't

get a word in, slow down." That was Brendan, once he started to speak; you had a job to shut him up.

"Right Brendan," I stood toe to toe with him, my hand over his mouth, "I'll tell you everything you want to know …if you just keep bloody quiet for a second or two." My voice rising with frustration and him still trying to mumble through my hand, but with a struggle he finally stopped.

I filled the big feller in with as much news as I thought he could handle at one time, then quickly turned the tables on him by asking him a few questions of my own, like why hadn't he called to see me and the family sooner? "Be Jesus Tom, I have some great news, great news so it is," he repeated. I was standing there listening to him, in his broad Irish accent and realised how much I'd missed this great lump of an Irishman.

"Come on then," I beckoned, "What's this news." "Well now, I don't know if I should be telling yer or not so ah don't," he turned his head away slightly stroking his chin at the same time,

"What should yer not be telling me Brendan." "Dat I've got meself a girlfriend so a have." He stood there, open-mouthed for a brief moment.

"Be Jesus yerve gone an dun it again, so yer have, av told yer what ah wasn't gunna tell yer in der first place," he huffed, kicking a stone that lay near his feet. After Brendan stopped cussing and swearing for letting out his secret, he finally told me he was seeing a girl from the next village and that he had strong feelings for her.

When it came to looks, Brendan was at the back of the queue, a misshapen nose from all the fights he'd been in matched his cauliflower ears and one or two facial scars, plus a gap in his top teeth you could drive a bus through.

Brendan was no catch to say the least and I shuddered to think what type of girl he could attract! I had hardly let the thought go from my mind, when he suggested Jill and I meet him in the Pig and Whistle pub in two day's time. This was a local watering hole frequented by the dog racing lads, about four miles away in a little village called Salters Way. We bid our farewells after more vigorous hand shaking.

"Don't you be forgetting Tom, see yer in a couple of days," he shouted, as he walked away. Not that I'd dare forget.

I arrived home to find we had company, my old friend Jacob. I hadn't seen Jacob to have a good chat since the day after his shop was burned, except for the odd occasion we'd bumped into each other in the street.

The beating he had taken from Herman and his cronies told on his skeletal figure, the scars still visible on his worn old face. I stretched over to shake his hand.

"Mind the tea my boy that your lovely wife has gone to the trouble to make, now you want to go and spill it, sit, sit down already." I sat down opposite Jacob, just looking at the old man admiring his guts and character; his big black hat was stuck firmly on his head with his long grey hair resting on his shoulders. He dipped his biscuit into his tea then started to tell me the reason for his visit.

"I've called to tell you that my little shop at last will be open in a few days, it has taken a long time Tom my boy, if you or your good wife want anything for yourselves or the young ones, you will be most welcome." I was just about to say something when Jacob interrupted me.

"Before you say anything Tom Watson my dear, it is my

40

way of saying thank-you, I won't hear another word said on the matter my boy." Jacob pointed his long thin finger at me. "Not another word," he repeated. With that, he stood up, thanked Jill for the tea and left.

The following day, after I'd seen to the dogs I called in to see Jacob, he was putting the finishing touches to something he'd been working on and looked exhausted.

Jacob didn't visit my house that often and I thought there might have been some other reason for letting Jill and myself know about his little shop opening. After a few well placed questions I'd put to the old man I was satisfied there was no problem. Jacob placed the garment on which he was working onto the bench. "Cup of tea my boy, sit, sit," he insisted,

"I'm just making a brew Tom." We sat talking about the everyday things that we took for granted, when he started to tell of some of the horrors that had occurred while he was in captivity. The horrific things that the Germans had done to him and his people were heartbreaking.

Although Herman's name had not been mentioned in any of the conversation, I think what Jacob was trying to tell me was, no matter what that scumbag did he couldn't hurt him.

Jacob took out his wallet and glanced at the old and tattered photographs of his parents and siblings, he sat there deep in thought stroking his beard, the tears quite visible rolling down his old and worn face, to be honest... my tears weren't to far behind.

Then as if nothing had been said, he changed the subject and talked about anything and nothing as if he had been in a trance, how were the kids, how was Jill, he had just seen them the night before. I finished off my tea and bid the old man goodbye. "Don't forget Tom my boy, if at any time you or your family want anything, anything at all, you come and see me." I knew Jacob was a man of his word, with a family like mine; no doubt his services would be needed at some time.

On arriving home and telling Jill that I'd called in to see Jacob, I suddenly realized I'd forgotten to tell her about Brendan. After telling her about him working in Germany and finding himself a girlfriend---She just couldn't believe it and burst out laughing.

"Brendan with a girlfriend," Jill said, still not being able to contain her laughter. "Well---is she German." "No," I replied. "She's from the next village, Salters Way and before you take on another laughing fit! We're meeting him--- and her, tomorrow in the Pig and Whistle." Jill looked stunned--- her laughter had ceased. "But---but Tom," she stuttered, I---er can't, I---er I'm going to my mothers." "That's all right then," I replied.

"You'll be sitting in your mam's house by yourself." "How do you work that one out Mr clever clogs," she said giving me one of her smarmy looks.

"Because your mam and dad are away on the club trip." There was silence for about twenty seconds, her temper ready to explode, she stood up, stamped her foot and angrily pointed a finger at me, she was ready to explode.

"If you think I'm going into that so called pub---you've got another think coming, the reputation that place has, I, I, wouldn't allow one of the dogs to step foot in there."

Things were getting a bit heated, I had no idea that Jill had such a dislike for the Pig and Whistle, I managed to calm her down while I made a cup of tea.

"Now then what's all this fuss about a pub," I asked. "Its not just the pub Tom, it's the reputation the place has, along with the people that are supposed to be connected to it." Jill was right to have her doubts about the pub, there were strong rumours from the wise lads that Herman had something to do with the taking over of the Pig and Whistle.

The rumours were that the landlord Simon Long had been made an offer he couldn't refuse. Simon was a nice quiet lad; we had grown up together and worked down the pit from leaving school. From day one down that mine it was obvious that the manual work and the muck and dust was not for Simon. After a few years of hating the pit, it was both sad and a relief for Simon when his father died and left him the pub.

Simon's dad was a tough old stick and took no nonsense from anyone. His son certainly wasn't a chip off the old block. He was mild mannered and soft, anything for a quiet life. To be honest, a few others and I suspected Simon as being the other way. Not that it made any difference to me, but there were certain people who would exploit this situation, such as that scumbag Herman.

I tried to reassure Jill that Herman was long gone and had nothing to do with the pub, but deep down he was never far from my mind. After some persuading Jill finally gave in and agreed to meet Brendan and his girlfriend. I think curiosity was getting the better of her; she just had to see what Brendan's girlfriend looked like.

"Right Tom," said Jill, trying to look all stern and serious. "We'll have our usual shandy and that's it, I won't stop in that place any longer than need be," with that, she about turned without saying another word, tripping over one of the kids boots on her way to the bathroom, her head held so high.

The next day everything was back to normal, Jill was her usual self, singing to the radio as we set the kids off to school before going back to the kennels to finish off our chores, brushing the dogs, cleaning their teeth and so on. Then it was off for a long walk. I could sense Jill wanted to talk about meeting Brendan and his girlfriend at the pub, but I was playing Jill at her own game and ignored the situation all the way back to the kennels.

Every time Jill was about to say something I would start a conversation about the dogs, the kids, the weather, anything at all, just to keep her off the subject of Brendan and his girlfriend. In the end she gave up. "Right Tom Watson, you win," she stormed. "I'll find out everything I want when I see it for myself in that---. that, so called pub." With that off her chest, she set about her work in the kennel in silence.

That night, while we both got dressed to meet Brendan and his girlfriend, not a word was spoken, not for the want of trying on my behalf, I did my best, but when Jill was in one of those moods, it could last a very long time.

We heard the back door open and close.

"It's just me," shouted Doris, I'm knackered dashing up from that club trip at such short notice." We ambled downstairs, still not speaking.

Doris had only been in a few minutes and sensed something was wrong; she gave me one of her looks, then transferred the same look to Jill.

"Right you two," she said, the scowl on her face like a smacked arse. "You can cut the atmosphere with a knife in here and if you both think I'm going to baby-sit these kids, while you two have faces like fifty shilling pittle pots... you've got another think coming, you've got ten seconds to start speaking." I looked at Jill, she half looked at me.

"Make that five seconds." Doris walked over to pick up

her coat, the kids watching in anticipation; she was just about to open the door to leave, when both Jill and I said at the same time,

"There's er no problem Doris, mam, no problem at all," we spluttered. "No problem mam," said Jill, "Just a silly misunderstanding."

It was time for a quick exit before things started to get complicated. We kissed the kids goodbye, Jill kissed her mother, I looked at Doris for a few seconds, then thought---no I'll just wave goodbye, Doris in that sort of mood was liable to do anything, like throw the odd punch, or knee you in the groin, I thought best not take the risk and left waving goodbye through the window.

At least Doris had broken the ice for us to start speaking. On the way to the pub Jill had a million questions. What did this girl look like? Had she been married before? How old was she? Did she have any kids? Jill was still talking when we arrived at the Pig and Whistle.

We walked through into the bar, the whole room went quiet for a few seconds---the looks we were getting made us want to about turn and head back home. But I thought to myself, shit, I've come this far to see my old mate I'm staying.

As quick as the talking had stopped, it started again, it wasn't because we were strangers, there were lots of doggie men in there that recognized us.

I think the reason for the silence was that we rarely frequented the pubs, as we were both non-drinkers. I ordered two half shandy's from the barmaid then sat down.

"No sign of Brendan and his girlfriend," said Jill, giving me one of those looks. A very slow ten minutes had gone by, still no sign of the elusive two, I looked around the pub once more just to make sure I hadn't missed them. In a corner tucked away having a drink and a laugh with some of the lads was a well known face, a young lady, I say that with great reservation with the nickname of Vinegar Lill.

She obtained the name through the face she pulled when drinking whisky, her favourite tipple, no sips, straight back, then she'd screw up her face, close her eye's, her chin would nearly touch her nose, not a pretty sight I might add.

Jill had also caught sight of Lill, commenting on her jewellery, rings on most of her fingers, a pearl necklace and large earrings. We were just about to leave, when in walked Brendan.

"Be Jesus Tom, I taught yer might be gone so I did, I had tu go and pick up der girlfriend," he gasped, as he sat down to catch his breath.

"Well, where is she," I asked, looking behind Brendan expecting her to be following him in. "Well dat's der ting Tom, I'm off tu pick her up, when her next door neighbour says she's off tu meet me in the Pig and Whistle." That was Brendan; you could bet your life if he could get it wrong, he would.

"Looks like she stood you up Brendan, there's only a few of the dog men in and Vin," I was just about to say Vinegar Lill, when Brendan stood up and shouted.

"Der's der light of me life, sitting right der so she is." To my horror, Brendan looked in the direction of the only other woman in the pub, Lill.

Jill had a look on her face of sheer *shock* as she sat motionless in her seat, not being able to move or speak, her eyes in a trance like focus.

Brendan made a beeline towards Lill, grabbed her hand just as she was about to down another whisky. "Brendan Kerr," snarled Lill. "Yer can thump me, or kick me, even break me nose if yer like, but never, never... stop me in midstream when I'm drinking whisky, du yer realize how dangerous that could be," exclaimed Lill, sitting there with a grip like a vice on her glass.

"Ah could have spilled some of that," she screeched angrily. Brendan looked at Lill and paused for a while..."Be Jesus yer right Lill, ah just wasn't tinking, I'm sorry me darling, so I am."

"So yer should be yer great oaf," said Lill screwing up her face as the last drop of whisky left her glass.

Making sure the glass was completely empty Brendan dragged Lill over to make the introductions.

After about twenty minutes chat Jill and (Maxine), Lill's correct name were getting on like a house on fire, it turned out that Max, as she liked to be called, had arrived from Ireland about fifteen years ago and was living in a little village called Maltdale, six miles from where Jill and I lived. There was one pub, about ten houses with a little shop that sold everything and anything, from groceries to coal and oil for the lamps.

Max explained to Jill she had fallen pregnant not long after arriving from Ireland, the result a son, who was nearing his sixteenth birthday.

After an unexpectedly pleasant evening we bid our farewells to Max and Brendan, with the pair promising to keep in touch. I had the feeling that the promise would not be broken by the big feller and his girlfriend and looked forward to seeing them again.

As Jill and I left the pub, we bumped into my old mate

Simon Long, tall, good-looking and never a hair out of place. Simon was the owner of the pub. He was pleased to see us and shook my hand vigorously. In a few seconds the expression of joy on his face turned to the gaunt look of a worried man.

"You feeling alright Simon," I asked. "Its just yer looking a bit washed out me old mate." Simon wiped the sweat from his forehead as he glanced swiftly over his shoulder.

I was determined to find out what the problem was, illness or fear. I asked if he would be more comfortable and at ease if we went somewhere a bit more discreet. Simon shrugged his shoulders and said "Some other time," quickly glancing over his shoulder as if he were expecting someone to be watching him. He made his excuses before hurriedly making his way into the pub and up the stairs. Sooner or later I had the feeling Simon would be knocking at my door.

CHAPTER SEVEN

Still no sign of Herman. We had kept in touch with Brendan and Max, Jill had made a good friend of Maxine, even though she liked her drop of whisky, she had a heart of gold.

Max never came to our house without a bag of sweets for the kids and a few groceries for Jill. Jill would often feel embarrassed and try to refuse, saying that Max could ill-afford them. "Plenty more where they came from," would be Max's reply. Jill and I would often say to each other, how and where was she getting these groceries, how could she afford them? We'd look at each other and shake our heads then say - --we don't want to know, and then leave it at that.

Spotty was due to come into season at any time, all the tell tale signs were there. She always ran well when she was due to come into season, so we wanted to enter her in a race as soon as possible.

Looking through the dog paper I noticed they required entries at Downhill Track, belonging to Mr and Mrs Ryan.

I liked the Ryan's and it was pretty obvious there was a shortage of dogs entered at their track, probably due to the amount of handicaps going on at the other tracks. It worked like this; it was a ploy most of the tracks played to keep as many dogs entered at their own tracks as possible.

All dogs were in handicaps, the first second and third dogs go through to the next round, this kept them at that track for a good three weeks, stopping you from racing your dog elsewhere, hence the shortage of dogs at the Ryan's track.

We rang the Ryan's and entered Spotty for this unfilled race on the card,

"Is dat you Tom Watson," said the voice. "It is Mr Ryan."

"Well Tom, yer know how the procedure works."

"I do Mr Ryan," I replied.

"The dogs are put into a race as they are entered and den handicapped accordingly to their capabilities, I might tell yer young Tom, yer lucky so yer are, der's only one more entry required in your race and dat's a full meeting so it is, good luck to yer and I'll be seeing yer at der track so ah will."

The next night, Jill myself and the kids, along with Spotty piled into the van and set off for the track, it was one of those nights when the fog was lifting then falling, it didn't know what to do and I hated it. Jimmy and his son Terry were there along with Billy and Ray Foster.

The first thing Terry did when he saw me was ask if I had a question for him about the sixties, if my memory serves me right I had told Terry the last time I had seen him that I would have a question for him. I had no idea what to ask, I was really struggling when Billy came to the rescue.

"Who was top in 1965." Before Billy could take a breath, Terry had told him who was top, how many records they had sold and when the recording artists birthday was. Terry's a truly remarkable young man, as soon as he had delivered the answer, he dragged his father off to the track canteen, that was something else Terry was very good at---eating.

We sat down in the canteen to study the race Spotty was competing in. I was shocked when scrolling down the runners with my finger I saw the name *MONTY,* it wasn't the amount of yards she was giving away, that wasn't the problem--- it was this villain of a dog that should never be allowed to run on any track. The dog had fought and injured so many dogs it didn't bear thinking about.

Mr Ryan, who was walking past could see I was none too pleased. "Tom, me lad, ah can see yer not to happy so yer not, be Jesus if I could have made tings different I would have." He went on to explain that our race was the last race to be filled and that Monty the villain, was the last dog to be entered.

"I couldn't say tu der man der's no more dogs wanted, he could see der last place was waiting tu be filled so it was, tu be honest Tom, if I'd put him in someone's else's race dat wouldn't be right either, now would it?"

I knew the old man was right, but it didn't make me feel any better or alter the situation.

There was only one thing to do, seek out the lads who owned Spotty and ask them to make the decision whether to run her or not.

Martin was there along with the rest of the group, but no Phill, he was off on holiday with his wife. I explained the situation to Martin; he said he would put the question to the rest of the group. It wasn't long before he was back with an answer.

"We've have had a bit of chat Tom and we've taken a vote." Both Jill and I waited with bated breath,

"Well," I said, looking Martin straight in the eye.

"It's like this Tom, said Martin looking down and kicking the ground like a schoolboy being ticked off by the headmaster, then he mumbled something about the bitch.

"Martin, what did you say, something about the bitch running? I hope it wasn't what I thought you said."

"I'm afraid you heard right Tom, the lads think she should

51

take her chance because she's too good for the likes of dodge pots like Monty." By this time both Jill and I were ready for walking out of the track... with the bitch, then I got a little reminder from one of the syndicate.

"Watson, you don't own the bitch, you get paid for training her, we say if she runs or not."

This was coming from the mouth of a toffee nosed little shit who had just joined the betting shop from another branch, he was the nephew of Phill's wife, a smarmy spoilt brat, who looked right out of place in his toff's suit and dickey bow tie.

Phill loved the dogs, but he also jumped when his wife told him too. It was pointless trying to argue with someone who didn't know which end of a dog to feed. I was struggling to keep my temper, maybe it was the way Jill and Billy had a tight grip on both of my arms, or the kids looking on and the thought of spending a night in the cells.

I stood there contemplating whether to follow through with my thoughts, when I felt a slight tug on my coat and a voice saying, "Go on dad, chin him." It was our youngest Paul. I glanced down and shook my head, a smile forming on my face at the suggestion coming from our youngest to chin him. The rush of blood rescinded and the look on Jill's face brought me back to normality.

I pushed past the group to where the creep with the mouth and attitude was standing and whispered.

"If anything happens to this bitch tonight, you will have great difficulty in trying to father a child...that's when and if you ever get someone stupid enough to marry yer." I had a tight grip on his manhood, not that there was much to grip onto unawares to the lads standing behind me. The blood drained from his face, then a look of relief as I loosened the grip from his meat and two veg.

The loudspeaker crackled into action, it was time for Spotty's race, maybe the lads were right after all she was the fastest dog in the race! But I had yet to see a slow dodgy fighter, I knew this dog was a real villain; I had one of those feelings that things weren't right. As I walked towards the paddock the owner of Monty, a rough looking character, unshaven and teeth like piano keys crossed my path then commented.

"You won't win this race Watson, my Monty will murder that bitch of yours." He was one of those blokes that nobody liked, greedy, cruel when his dog got beaten in a race, a real bad character.

"How much do you want for that dog Smithy," I asked, before he and the dog got to the paddock. My idea was to buy the dog and then withdraw him from the race making the excuse the dog was injured.

I knew this man's reputation for being greedy and always short of cash. Smithy stopped dead in his tracks.

"How much will you pay Watson," he snarled.

"How much do yer want," I replied. Thinking to myself the dog is not worth two-bob, but I had the feeling this wasn't going to be easy.

"Try a £150 Watson," he said with a smarmy grin on his face. "Try kissing my arse," I replied, much to the disgust of an old lady walking past to whom I immediately apologized.

"The dog is not for sale Watson, not even if you wanted tu pay the £150, I'm going to win this race and show you and your Bookie friends that you can't win in the shops and at the track." There was something bugging this chap, it was more than just wanting to win this race. Then he blurted it out, it transpired that he had lost his wages in one of Phill's betting shops and got himself locked up in the local nick for beating up his wife. This was Smithy's way of revenge.

No matter how much money we were prepared to pay, Smithy was hell-bent on running his dog. We proceeded to the paddock where we placed the jackets and muzzles onto the dogs, I had one of those bad gut feelings that just wouldn't go away. I was all for turning round and forgetting about the race, when the announcement came to take the dogs to the traps.

Spotty had the number one Jacket the Red, she was the dog that would lead the parade, I felt all eye's were on me, I seemed to freeze for a brief moment before the loudspeaker crackled into action.

"Take dem dogs tu der starting traps please." You would think Spotty could understand Mr Ryan's announcement as she pulled me towards the traps.

Maybe I was being a little paranoid. Spotty was the best dog in the race and with her track skill hopefully everything would turn out all right.

Everyone stood behind their allocated trap and waited for the announcement for the dogs to be placed into the traps. Smithy's dog Monty was snarling and growling at anything that came near it.

"That muzzle had better be on that dog of yours properly Smithy," said one of the owners knowing of the reputation Monty had for fighting on the track. Smithy just glanced at the man and smirked---- "Place the dogs into the traps," called Mr Ryan.

The dogs were placed into the traps and the hare was running, swish went the hare as it rattled past the traps. Spotty came out well and was soon just behind the top two runners who were receiving eight and nine yards start. Monty, Smithy's dog was too busy trying to fight anything and everything within reach and that suited Spotty. The dogs were at the last bend, Spotty had just taken the lead, her usual two lengths in front and that's how they crossed the line.

First trap one, second trap four and third trap six. With a big sigh of relief, I made my way across the track to the trip where the dummy hare had stopped. One of the young lads had caught hold of Spotty and held her until I reached them.

Smithy caught hold of his dog Monty by his muzzle then started beating the hell out of the poor animal with its lead. Not happy striking the dog he then started kicking him with his hob nailed boots. In fear and panic the dog pulled away, leaving Smithy holding an empty muzzle.

Then all hell broke loose, Monty made a beeline for the nearest dog to him---which just happened to be Spotty. He worried her to the ground in a frenzied attack despite of the efforts of those and myself trying stop him. After I'd been bitten several times trying to protect the bitch from a blood crazed Monty the dog was finally restrained.

I stood over Spotty, as she lay there motionless, covered in blood. I looked up to see Smithy without a flicker of remorse on his face. I knew it was the wrong thing to do, but I couldn't help myself. I grabbed him by his white silk scarf and pulled him to the ground, beating the shit out of him. His scarf covered in blood that was pouring from his nose. I was like a madman possessed raining blows onto his body as he lay on the ground.

I just couldn't stop hitting him. I was finally pulled away still trying to strike out at the man, my hands and clothes dripping with blood.

Mr Ryan arrived along with the vet of the same name---Jill, Billy and Jimmy had made their way over to the trip only to be held back by one or two of the lads that had dogs in the race.

"It's best if you keep back Jill, you'll only get yourself upset bonny lass," said Tony Short, the trapper on the night.

The vet was an Irish cousin of the Ryan's, a good vet that I had dealt with many times.

After checking on the condition of Spotty he made his way over to where I was being restrained.

"It's not good news Tom me lad, not good news at all," he said shaking his head as he looked at the ground shaking his head. "I'm ---er---I'm afraid the wee bitch is dead Tom."---I stood there in a daze, thinking this can't be true, not Spotty, not the pet of the whole kennel. "If der is a small consolation Tom," said the vet, " It's dat she went quick--- it wasn't the wounds dat killed her ----it was der shock."

We took Spotty home and buried her at the bottom of the garden, a stark reminder of the hazards of dog racing. I'd been in this position before, digging a hole and breaking my heart at the same time, it was the worst feeling I'd ever had.

Things weren't the same after that, the kennel where Spotty stayed lay empty and dark, that's just the way I felt inside. The lads from the betting shop came round to see me and Jill, that is all but the jerk that wanted Spotty to run that night. Apparently he'd asked to be transferred to another shop down south ---for some reason or other.

The lads were sick about the whole situation and wanted to buy another dog to replace Spotty, but how could you replace a dog like her!

It would have been unfair to try to kid ourselves and the lads that any other dog could take the place of Spotty.

My heart wasn't in it and I felt it would be some time before Jill and myself could bring ourselves to get back into the routine we were in before Spotty's death. We had to make a decision, kick ourselves up the backside and get on with it! Or get out of the game altogether!

We were discussing our situation when Billy my best mate came in the back door. Since the loss of Spotty, Billy had been helping out more than ever at the kennels. "Tom, Jill," he nodded as he slipped off his boots and sat down in the old armchair. "Cup of tea Bill," Jill asked, still down in the mouth about the bitch. Billy picking up the vibes between Jill and myself decided to get one or two things off his chest.

"Right you two, you both have faces like fifty shilling piss pots and you've been like that since we lost Spotty, we all miss that little bitch, but things have to move on, so get on with it---or pack the bloody game in." Billy was pulling his boots back on, snapping one of the laces in sheer frustration.

"I'll tell you something else while I'm on, the little black pup Lucky, is screaming for a run and what are you doing about it, moping about the place or sitting on your arse's.

Billy marched through the door and left Jill and myself gob smacked, we had never seen him like this before. Billy reacting the way he did made us realize we had to take a good look at ourselves, we knew he was right ---it was time to move on.

CHAPTER EIGHT

Brendan and Maxine had called in to see if we would like to pop round to her house tomorrow as she was having a small party for her son Nathan's sixteenth birthday. Maxine and Jill had become very good friends, so we readily accepted the invitation.

As Jill and I arrived at Maxine's house the following day young Nathan was just leaving.

"Nice to see you Mr, Mrs Watson, I'm just off to Mr Hobson's shop, I was there yesterday but forgot one or two things that my mam needed, I won't be long," he shouted as he raced off at pace down the street.

Hobson the grocer had been there since I was a lad, a miserable mean old fart who never had the time of day for anyone, you know the type, turns off the gas when turning over the bacon to try and save a copper or two.

Nathan had left the door open so we knocked and walked straight in to be greeted by a vigorous handshake from Brendan and a sloppy kiss from Maxine.

"Nice tu see yer Tom, Jill, now will yer be sitting down --- or will yer be standing up, as der's not a lot tu be sitting on." Brendan was right, there wasn't a seat to be found. Young Nathan was more popular than we had thought, when we had a good look round, there weren't a lot of kids his age it was nearly all grown up's with a few toddlers.

Maxine introduced Jill and I to the others, mostly neighbours. Stuck away in a corner of the room were two of

the queerest characters you would ever set eye's on---
Stringvest Willie and Anytime Annie. Willie, a short stout
chap with a face a dog wouldn't lick, wearing a smart black
two-piece suit, the jacket slightly on the tight side.

For Willie to have a suit that matched---somebody must
have died and he was wearing the deceased clothes. Willie
refused nothing, big or small, short or tall, it made no
difference.

As for Annie, what can I say about Annie! She was just the
opposite to Willie in proportion. Tall, thin, something like a
pipe cleaner with arms and legs. As for her make-up, she'd
either tried to make herself up while having a bout of the
hiccups, or Willie's brakes on the car weren't what they
should have been. Either way she was a sight not to show the
kids before they went to bed.

Willie got his name because he never ever took his
stringvest off, no matter what the weather or the occasion,
funerals or weddings, you would see the vest through the
white nylon shirt with a small cigarette burn just below the
collar, no doubt Annie's handy work.

The only other time Willie was parted from his vest was in
the showers at the pit after a hard shift. When he went on
holiday to Spain, the weather scorching hot, but the dreaded
vest never left his body.

Willie's first day back at the pit after his holiday was a
right laugh, at the end of his shift, Willie's in the shower
standing there looking like a sieve, the full pattern of his
string vest imprinted onto his body. Everyone looking at him
and shaking their heads, Willie just standing there with his
arms outstretched, saying---- "What----what." To Willie
everything was normal.

As for his girlfriend Annie, I'll leave it to your imagination why they called her Anytime Annie? We were all ushered into the parlour where Vinegar Lill (Maxine) had laid out a cracking spread; she had done young Nathan proud. It was easy to see why there were so many neighbours and to be honest, who could blame them, the only time there was a spread like that, cooked ham, cream cakes and the like, was when there was a wedding or a funeral.

All the grown-ups sat at the table, the kids in a separate room and already getting stuck into the food. "Be Jesus can yer not be waiting for der birthday boy himself," shouted Brendan. This put a startled look on some of the smaller kids faces -----but only for a brief moment, then they were tucking in like it was some sort of race.

Just then Nathan entered the room after his errand down to Mr Hobson's shop, a puzzled look on his face.

"What's up son," asked Maxine, an equally puzzled look on her face.

"Did yer not get the tings at Mr Hobson's, asked his mother.

"He wouldn't give them to me, mar, he was talking all gibberish." "He said I had to pass a message on to you." The room fell silent, waiting for Nathan to give the message from Mr Hobson to his mother.

"Well, Well," beckoned Maxine. Nathan standing there trying to compose himself. "Let me get this straight mar, what Mr Hobson said was." By now everyone had leaned forward and were on the edge of their seats.

"He said--- tell your mother that I know you are sixteen to-day---and that there will be no more free groceries--- and when I tell you I have to look at the expression on your face!"

60

Maxine paused for a few seconds---- "Well son, you go back to Mr Hobson and you tell him this--- *he's not your father*---- and I'd like to see the expression on his *face*."

Everyone laughed loudly, that is all but Brendan, he had a puzzled look on that scraggy face of his. "Let me explain Brendan," said Max, with a smile and a wink of her eye.

"When I first came tu England I didn't have a penny in me pocket, lonely and broke I went tu work for Mr Hobson in der shop, one ting led to another and when he found out that he thought he'd made me pregnant, he kicked me out, but he did say I could have a weekly shop of groceries until Nathan was sixteen." Maxine paused for a moment, then continued with her story.

"He's kept his word right up tu der very day so he has--- but what he didn't know was dat I was pregnant when I arrived in England, I'd fallen out wit me boyfriend over der pregnancy, so dat's why I ended up here." Brendan looked dumbstruck. "But Max," said Brendan, scratching his head. "If dat scoundrel Hobson, tru you out in der street, where's der baby?" The room went silent. Brendan looked at Max waiting for an answer.

"Yer big eadit, he's looking at yer." Brendan in turn looking at each and every one of the kids, trying to work it out.

"Max der's no baby's in here!" said Brendan looking more puzzled than ever.

"Be Jesus are yer tick or someting," said Max again, starting to lose her temper.

"It's Nathan yer great oaf." "What's Nathan," said Brendan. "He's der baby I was carrying when I was pregnant." "Is dat so," said Brendan looking up and down at young

Nathan, everyone in the room in kinks of laughter. "I er –I knew dat so I did--I er, was just joking wit yer so I was."

Brendan was in a corner and the jibes came fast and furious, he took it all in his stride, until Anytime Annie had her twopenneth to say.

"I thought I was thick Brendan, but when I see you, I think I have a pretty good brain." Annie had been drinking and Max wasn't too pleased with one or two of her snide remarks about Brendan being thick.

Maxine was just about to say something, when Brendan stepped in. "Are yer calling me tick--- Annie," said Brendan with a scowl on his face. "Well put it this way Brendan, I think I have something between my ear's you haven't got."--- Brendan quick as a flash replied.

"Yer right Annie, yer have sometin ah haven't got ---- A moustache and a beauty it is at dat."

"He's got yer there Annie," said Willie as the room erupted with laughter. "Brendan hasn't got much of a moustache ---well not as good as yours anyway." Annie took one scowling look at Stringvest, then Brendan -----she looked around the room then said---- "Yer right Willie, my moustache is better than his."

The whole room fell quiet for about ten seconds and then erupted once again, even the kids were laughing.

"Yer right," said Willie, pleased he'd gotten away with a crack about Annie's moustache without receiving a backhander in response. "Lets all go down to the Pig and Whistle and sink a few pints." Annie and Max were the first to grab their handbags and coats. "What about money for the drinks," said Annie, coming to a sudden stop, a look of disappointment on her heavily made up face.

"I'll buy the drinks," said Willie, standing aloof, all five feet four of him looking round the room that had gone deathly silent on hearing his suggestion for buying the drinks.

"There's more chance of der Red Sea opening than you opening dat wallet of yours Willie," the voice was unmistakably that of Brendan who knew Willie from way back.

"You might be right Brendan me old pal, but I have a clean slate at the pub---starting from tu-day." Willie hadn't got the words from his mouth before Annie and Max were out of that door struggling to put on their coats and nearly falling over each other as they scrambled their way out into the street going towards the Pig and Whistle. Jill and I slipped quietly away, completely unnoticed in the mad rush to the pub. The kids unmoved by all the commotion were quite happy to get stuck into whatever food was left.

CHAPTER NINE

A couple of months had gone by since the party at Brendan and Maxine's, still no sighting of Herman. The black pup Lucky was turning out to be something special. Dare I start to think things were on the up and up, I wondered!

Lucky had won two races at the Ryan's track and in very fast times, not open class races but very near, the time was right for a change to another track. We entered him at a track we rarely visited about 40 miles away where the reputation for skulduggery by the handicapper was rife.

A friend of ours called Frank Mustard had informed us that the handicapper was sticking dogs in to win for his mates from the licensed tracks, right left and centre.

Frank unfortunately had been born with one leg shorter than the other and had worn a calliper from a very early age. He also told me he was having a hard time trying to make ends meet to support himself and his widowed mother.

He'd had a medical at the pit when he'd left school hoping to join the rest of the lads, but unfortunately he failed. Not to be beaten, Frank got himself a little stick business going, but it was never going to make him rich.

He told me that he had backed his little black dog Sooty, three times in small opens and been beaten each time by something the handicapper had drafted in for one of his mates from down South.

This seemed the right time to give Lucky his biggest test. We met Frank about half a mile from the track and gave him the dog with strict instructions to take good care of him.

"Frank, don't go mad betting this pup, he's only had a couple of races."

"Can't do any worse than I'm doing at the moment Tom," he said.

"From what you told me on the phone Tom you've got high hopes of this little feller, if you have high hopes, then so have I." With that Frank shoved a bundle of notes into my hand.

"No matter what happens Tom, get my money on, the luck has tu change sometime and he'll be a big price, especially as they'll think it's my dog Sooty," he shouted as he walked off towards his little van. I could understand Frank in one way, all he had was his gambling, he was a single lad, not that he was a bad looking young man, he felt that if a girl got close to him it was through pity about his leg. Frank couldn't handle that.

We arrived at the track with one race to go before Lucky's race, had a good look around the crowd to make sure there were no familiar faces, not that it would make any difference because hopefully no one would connect Frank to us, even if Lucky were to win. The announcement bellowed out over the speaker it was time for Lucky's race.

Frank had left £50 in my hand, Billy and Jimmy wanted £40 between them, I wasn't that sure, I kept my bet to £30 making it up to £120. There were six books so we decided to do three at £40 each. Frank's dog, (Lucky) opened up at three to one, he'd drawn the blue trap number two.

The big money had come for trap six also a black dog, a real smart looking animal. It wasn't long before the price for trap six Marble had gone completely. The bookmakers were starting to wise up to this handicapper and as soon as any hefty money came for a dog of suspicion, the price for that dog would be cleaned off.

"This must be a bloody handy dog Bill for the amount of money that's been shovelled onto him, I'm starting to think about halving my few quid." Lucky had gone to six to one, shit I thought to myself, sink or swim, we each picked out a bookmaker and took the best odds shown for Lucky.

The hare was on the move, swish as it passed the traps and up went the lids, Lucky stood his ground as he jostled for position at the first bend, brave as a lion he forced his way round the bend to come out second dog to number six Marble, just half a length behind him. This was a true test for Lucky, now we would find out just how good our little rescue pup was.

Rounding the third bend the dogs were neck and neck. Coming to the fourth and last bend I couldn't believe my eyes when Lucky took the lead with 50 yards to go.

"Go on my son; go on," I mumbled under my breath. There was no danger, Lucky passed the post first, winning by three lengths.

Frank could be both seen and heard screaming his head off and trying to do his best at running round the inner part of the track. As for the team who had backed the six dog Marble, there were some very queer looks in the direction of the handicapper's box and more so when the time for the race was called out.

Lucky had run just short of the track record by one and a half lengths. I was that delighted I nearly forgot to draw the winnings.

"There you are young man," said the bookmaker, a broad

smile on his chubby red face. "I'm delighted to be paying you out," he said, tipping his hat after counting out £280 into my hand.

Both Jimmy and Bill gathered their winnings, both had smiles as big as the bookmakers as we headed for the exit. "Can yer believe that time Tom," said Billy rubbing his hands with excitement. "Never mind the time lads, lets get up that road and out of sight before somebody puts two and two together and realises that the dog Frank had wasn't his."

We sped off to the meeting place we'd arranged with Frank beforehand. He was standing outside his little old van of many colours, different coloured doors, one red and the other blue, with a green bonnet, it was easy to see Frank was having a hard time of things just by the state of his van.

A man with the look of a football pools winner was waiting to greet us. "Tom is that some dog, or is that some dog," said Frank with a smile that could put everyone else's to shame. "I have to admit Frank, the dog has shocked me and the lads, that's three out of three races, where to next." Before I could break into the next sentence I was bombarded from all directions with suggestions from finding a ringer, to grading in and open racing.

Bill, Jimmy and Frank were right into the discussion of where the dog should go next, I stood back for a while, then took the dog from Franky's van, all unawares to the Brains Trust that were planning Lucky's next race. I made sure the dog was all right, then placed him in the back of my van. I sorted out Franky's money then slotted it into his glove compartment.

I started up the engine to the shock and bemusement of the three stooges and then proceeded to drive off.

"Your money's in the glove compartment Frank, thanks for a job well done I'll be seeing you." I'd gone about 50 yards with Billy and Jimmy the beard in hot pursuit. "Wait Tom----wait, I'm knackered, shouted Jimmy, struggling to catch his breath. I steadied to a slow pace, then just as they were catching up I'd speed up again.

"Don't take--- the urine Tom," or words to that effect, said Jimmy, coughing and spluttering like an old mule. I slowed the van down to a crawl before the Beard had a heart attack. Billy, on the other hand was as fit as a fiddle striding out with ease and having a sly grin at Jimmy as he passed him, walking backwards taking the mickey.

I stopped the van and the two of them scrambled in, well to be honest, Billy jumped in and the Beard fell in. "I might have won--- a few quid Tom, but I'm going to have a bloody heart attack before I can spend it," said Jimmy as he puffed away on his inhaler. "Just er-- remind me Jim, was it the dog that ran in that race or you," said Billy holding his hand up to his face waiting for a missile to be thrown from Jimmy's direction.

"All right you two, let me remind you there's a dog in this van and if anything happens to him, you'll both be walking home." Billy and Jim knew I wasn't kidding and put their hands in the air as if to surrender.

"That's better lads, now let's get this money sorted, then we can get off home and give Jill and the kids the good news.

We dropped Lucky off at kennels, washed his feet and gave him his grub, if Lucky could do anything better than run it was eat, in no time at all his dish was clean and we were on our way home.

I walked through the door to be greeted by Jill and the kids all wanting to know if Lucky had won his race or not.

"The little feller did well, very well," I replied. "Does that mean he won dad," said Paul a smile from ear to ear.

"Yes son that means he won." "Great," he shouted, "That means fish and chips." It would be a hard bet to call if I was to gamble on who would finish their food first, Lucky or Paul?

I gave some money to Colin our oldest boy to pop down to the chippy, he was just about to leave when everyone shouted in unison---*"Don't let Mrs Moffit put too much sssssalt on."* It was wrong to take the mickey out of Mrs Moffit, but she did have the worst stutter we had ever heard. As the night went on and everyone settled down, Jill suddenly jumped up.

"Tom," she shrieked, holding her face with both hands. "I forgot to tell you, Mick from Barnsley has been in touch, something about a black dog running very well down in Yorkshire." I rang Mick later that night after the kids had settled and gone to bed.

Mick was the bobby and a good friend who had helped in the capture of the gang that had stolen Spotty.

It had transpired that a good black dog had been running very well at one or two tracks in his area. Mick hadn't seen the dog for himself, or the connections that were running it--- but by all accounts the dog belonged to a team of Geordies--- and from the description given, one man stuck out amongst the rest! Yes you guessed it, that scum of the earth Herman.

His description well over 6ft, scar on his left cheek, and the unmistakeable tattooed swastikas on his hands, there was no mistake; Herman was back on the scene.

It had been some time since Herman had officially been seen in the North East, I suppose hoping he would never show his face in the area again would be a minor miracle that just wasn't going to happen.

I told Jill of the conversation with Mick, that Herman had been seen in Yorkshire. I was expecting the worst; but to my amazement she stood there with her hands on her hips, shrugged her shoulders and said, "What has to be, has to be, it's about time decent folk stood up to the likes of---of--- ah, never mind looking for a word Tom Watson, you know what I mean." I did know what Jill meant and I admired her all the more for thinking it, even if she couldn't find the swear word she was looking for. I gave her a big hug and we agreed to stand our ground together, no matter what the consequences. (*Deep in my thoughts I dreaded to think what those consequences might be*).

CHAPTER TEN

Lucky had notched up another good win in an open race, he was turning out to be a real handy little dog, especially when you think of the start to life he'd had, being thrown into a sack with his brothers and sisters to die. I often wondered to myself how the rest of his litter might have turned out had they survived. At least his life had been saved, put it down to luck, coincidence or the fact that old Ben made me drop the sack that had given life to his canine comrade, who knows?

Brendan had found himself another job on a building site locally. Maxine had got over not being able to pop along to Mr Hobson's for her groceries now that young Nathan had turned sixteen. Willie and Annie were still going strong, apart from the time when they had a bit of fall out after a night out at the pictures and a meal afterwards.

Jill, myself, Brendan and Maxine had decided to have a quiet night down at the pub to celebrate Lucky's win and Brendan's new job.

It was midweek and the pub was quiet. The silence was broken as Willie pushed through the swing doors with a face like thunder. Annie followed behind narrowly escaping the closing doors as she tried to apply her make-up on the move.

Willie's face didn't need any make-up, blown out red cheeks and a frown you could grow potatoes in, not a pretty sight. The pair plonked themselves down at our table without a word being spoken, not even looking at each other. Someone had to break the ice and it looked like being me.

"Problem folks," I asked looking at Willie then Annie.

"It's her," growled Willie looking daggers at Annie.

"It's not me," snapped Annie, "How can you blame me, ah didn't do anything," she said, still trying to apply her make-up.

"That's just the bloody point," said Willie spitting all over the place with anger. "You didn't bloody do anything!"

It was time to try to get to the bottom of this matter otherwise we could be here all night.

"Right Willie, is there any chance that one of you can explain what the problem is, otherwise our quiet night out is going to be even quieter because we are going to be off home and leave you two love birds to sort it out on your own." Both Willie and Annie looked at each other and said at the same time, "It's her." "It's him," they snapped.

"Right William," I pointed, you first." Willie straightened himself up, pulled at the neck of his string vest and cricked his head in an upward direction.

"It's like this Tom, we were standing in the queue for the pictures when I spotted a £5 note on the ground, it was nearer to *her* than me, pointing to Annie, so I told her to put her foot on the note then bend down and pick it up before anyone realised it was there."

Everyone leaned forward anxious to hear what happened next. "And," asked Brendan, a blank expression on his scraggy face prompting Willie to get on with the story. "I'm getting there, I'm getting there," repeated Willie, pulling once again at the neck of his string vest with his finger.

"Annie had done the hard bit picking up the note without being seen," said Willie shaking his head in disbelief. "So what's the problem," asked Brendan.

72

"I'll tell yer the problem Brendan, Miss Smart Arse put the £5 note down her bra for safe keeping." "Dat would be der right place tu be putting it so it would," interrupted Brendan. "My thoughts exactly," said Willie giving a look towards Annie that could kill.

"So what happened," asked Jill, curiosity eating away at her by the second. "I'll tell yer exactly what happened," said Willie. "But I want no more interruptions," giving Brendan a stern look.

"This is what happened, as I said Annie placed the £5 note down her bra, then after the pictures had finished we decided to have a meal at that new restaurant just around the corner.

"And," interrupted Brendan.

"Shut it Brendan," said Max "Or we will never get to the end of this bloody story."

"Thank you Max," said Willie, "I'll carry on, we pigged out with a cracking meal well worth the money, then I asked Annie to dig deep down her cleavage for the £5 note." Brendan was just about to say something when Max gave him one of her no nonsense stern looks. Willie carried on.

"After frantic searching and nearly a strip show, the £5 was nowhere to be found, this called for some quick thinking."

"The waiter must have had an idea something was wrong and that he wasn't going to be paid, especially after the near striptease."

"I whispered in Annie's ear, placed my arm around her shoulders as she started to gasp for air."

"Can I help in any way sir," asked the worried looking waiter.

"She's having an assumer attack mate, ah better take her

outside for some fresh air."

"Is that why the lady was loosening her clothing sir," asked the waiter, looking very concerned. "I that's it mate exactly, if yer can bring us a glass of water outside that would be champion, the waiter went one way tu the kitchen and we went the other way tu the main street, that's why ah looked knackered when ah came in and she was still putting on the war paint."

"So what happened to the £5 note," asked Jill. "Ah yes, the money," replied Willie. "Should ah tell them or will you," nodding in Annie's direction. "Carry on Willie boy," replied Annie, still trying to apply her make-up. "You're doing alright up tu now bonny lad, keep going." Willie carried on with the story. "After getting plenty of distance between us and that restaurant waiter, I asked Annie what had happened tu the note--- and this is what she said."

"She blamed it on the bloke sitting next to her in the pictures, so I asked her straight out, how the hell can yer blame the bloke sitting next tu yer." Willie paused and tried to compose himself then carried on with the story. "She tried to explain to me how she had let the man sitting next to her put his hand inside her blouse."

"I was gob-smacked with her answer," said Willie, as he continued with the story. "I asked Annie again to explain how she had let a complete stranger put his hand inside her *blouse.*" At that stage Annie abruptly interrupted Willie,

"Yes I did let the man put his hand inside me blouse --- but ah didn't know he was a bloody thief!"

The room went quiet for about twenty seconds, then erupted with hilarious laughter from everyone that was in the pub, that included Simon Long the landlord. For Simon to even smile these days was a rare occasion, there was something troubling that young man, but I just couldn't put my finger on it. To see Simon looking a bit happier was a bonus, to be honest everyone in the pub had a smile on their faces and with good reason. Only Annie could give an answer like that and think there wasn't a problem.

Brendan and myself were doubled up; the whole room was creased with laughter. Annie just sat there holding out her hands saying, "What, What," as if it was a natural occurrence for someone to put his hand inside her blouse. Lets face it; she wasn't nicknamed Anytime Annie without good reason!

It was all too much for Jill, Max, Brendan and myself, we finished our drinks and bid everyone goodnight, it was nice to see Simon, still with a broad grin on his face as we left. I had the feeling his joy would be short lived.

CHAPTER ELEVEN

News had reached the village that Herman had been seen locally. His protection racket and other money making activities had not ceased in his absence. The shopkeeper's were paying their dues to his henchman that is all but one, Jacob.

I feared the worst for the old man, his resilience and his determination not to give in to the likes of Herman was inspiring to say the least.

Herman's men would beat up one or two of the shopkeeper's who had not been able to keep up their payments, just as a reminder to the others to toe the line.

But for some unknown reason Jacob and his shop had been untouched, that worried me a lot. Not that it would make any difference to the old man, no matter what happened he wouldn't give an inch to Herman or anyone else, as had been proved in the past.

Saturday afternoon Jill, the kids and myself were walking down to the village shops. The kids were in competition with each other to see who could make the biggest sparks on the old cobblestones with their hobnail boots. I remember my old gran showing me photographs of street parties held in the village when she was just a young girl and the cobbles were there then.

We were just about to pop into old Jacob's shop when he appeared at the door. "Tom, Jill, little ones come in, come in already," he said. "How very nice to see you, " half bobbing his head as if we were some sort of royalty.

We were just about to enter the shop when a car screeched to a sudden stop right outside the door of Jacobs little shop. To our horror, out stepped Herman and three of his cronies. The kids knowing of this mans reputation stood behind Jill and myself, peeping round from behind our bodies.

"Right Watson," growled the scar-faced bully towering head and shoulders above Jacob, Jill and myself.

"You, you little bastard," he shouted pointing at me. I stopped him dead in his tracks before he could utter another word. " Hold on there big man, you might be right and I am a little bastard," I replied. "Unfortunately I was an accident at birth, but you Herman--- *you are a self-made bastard."*

That was enough to make the bully lose his temper as he kicked over a table of fruit and veg next door to Jacob's shop.

"Ah think I've upset him Jill," I said sarcastically.

"Bet your bloody life you've upset him," replied Jill gripping tightly onto my arm.

"Problem is--- what happens next."

I feared the worst and ushered Jill and the kids into Jacobs shop, I was looking for something to defend myself when the cavalry arrived in the shape of my old mate Brendan.

He had seen the crowd gathering outside Jacob's shop and thought the old man might be in some sort of trouble.

Luck was on our side that Max had instructed Brendan to call into the village for a little shopping on his way home from work. It was also lucky for us that Brendan had finished work early and decided to call into the butchers first, that was on the opposite side of the road to Jacobs shop. It was only when he forced his way to the front of the crowd that he got his eye on me Jill and the kids.

"Tom me boy, what would all der fuss be about then."

"None of your business carrot head," growled one of Herman's lackeys as he moved towards Brendan snarling like an animal. *Big mistake mister, I thought to myself as the man drew closer to his fate.* "Would you be referring tu der redness of me hair young feller."

"What do you think yer thick Irish bastard," replied the lackey. Brendan lurched forward with his head, down went the man like a ton of bricks, his nose splattered all over his face, pouring blood profusely.

"There yer are now, yer have a nose nice and red, der same as me nice red hair so yer have." Herman looking frustrated sent in his next man only for him to suffer the same fate as his comrade.

"Be Jesus I'm just getting into me stride so I am," said Brendan rubbing his hands together as he shuffled his feet like a boxer. "Which one of yer clowns is next?" The last of Herman's cronies pushed forward fists up in front of his face, wary of Brendan's head butting power, but Brendan had more experience than just head butting. He'd been brought up in Ireland in the gypsy camps and did his fair share of bare knuckle fighting as he grew from youth to a hardened experienced fighter who was not to be messed with epically when someone had insulted him and his country.

Brendan let loose with an all mighty blow to the man's ribs, he fell to the ground in agony clutching his side screaming "Me ribs, me ribs, he's broken me ribs, boss get me to a doctor ah-- ah can't breath."

Herman stood there looking at the man writhing in agony, then gave him a mighty kick to the stomach, then one to the face.

"If yer can't deal with the likes of him, yer no good tu me." Herman was just about to leave when he caught sight of Jacob.

"Don't think your problems are over Jew, because they have just started."

Then the strangest thing happened. Herman came out with the most peculiar words I have ever heard. I presumed they were German, at least they sounded like German. Pointing to Jacob in the most aggressive manner and screaming at the top of his voice he shouted,

"*Verrkaufen sie tiefkihlkost.*" Brendan and Jacob looked at each other for a second or two then burst out in fits of laughter, much to the amazement of both Herman and the crowd. I hadn't seen Jacob laugh like that in all the time that I had known him, a wheezy sort of silent laugh.

Brendan's was just the opposite, deafening raucous and unforgettable.

"Well, which one of you two is going to stop laughing long enough to tell us the joke?" I asked.

"The joke Tom, my boy, is on that fool standing there," said Jacob pointing at Herman.

"The man who thinks he's German has just asked me do I- -- do I sell FROZEN FOODS." The crowd were in uproar, Herman left in total embarrassment, slamming his car door, smoke rising from the burning tyres skidding on the old cobblestones as he screeched off leaving his man writhing on the ground.

Brendan and Jacob were still bent over in fits of laughter. The crowd were mumbling among themselves with delight that the tables had at last been turned on Herman, at least for the time being.

Jill was more concerned about the condition of Herman's man, still moaning and groaning in agony. "He might be one of Herman's henchmen Tom, but you wouldn't leave a dog in pain like this, would yer, for God's sake someone phone for an ambulance," she shouted.

"Thank you lady," groaned the man, "I owe you a favour," he gasped, before passing out.

We waited at the scene until the ambulance arrived, blue lights flashing as he braked outside of Jacob's shop. "What's happened here then," asked the driver looking for a response from crowd, the crowd in turn looked at each other.

"Slipped-- on der cobbles so he did," said Brendan looking for support from the people standing there, everyone nodded in agreement.

"Slipped did he, was this after the bus hit him or before, cos he's in a bonny mess and if me memory serves me right it must have been the same sort of bus that hit this feller a few weeks ago when ah had tu pick him up from a fight after a disturbance?"

It was obvious this chap was not cut out for the sort of action expected of Herman's team. The ambulance sped off with siren sounding loudly. At least there was no police involvement; we all had our suspicions of Herman's connections with certain policemen and with good reason.

I dreaded to think of what kind of situation we'd have been in if Brendan hadn't stopped to do a bit of shopping. Both Jacob and I thanked the big Irishman for his help and I asked if he wanted to pop up to our house for a cupper, he had a quick look at his watch and shook that ginger mop of hair.

"Be Jesus look at der time, if I'm not home in twenty minutes wit der shopping I'll be facing a bigger scrap wit

Maxine than dem tree fellers, der problem is I'm not forced tu be beaten Maxine so am not." I shook Brendan's hand and told him I'd see him at the track on Monday.

"I'll keep yer tu dat Tom and if der's any more problems you'll let know me so yer will, good luck Tom, good luck," he shouted. He dashed off to the shops like a schoolboy hurrying home before getting a clip from his mother for being late.

Brendan was right when he said good luck, which was the right word on this occasion. It could have been myself, or poor Jacob in that ambulance. I'm not a religious person but that night I said a big thank you to the man upstairs.

All that weekend both Jill and I kept an extra eye on the kids and the dogs. Herman had been humiliated beyond belief. If he was to keep his reputation intact he would be looking for some sort of revenge.

Monday morning, the kids were off to school no problem, the dogs were fine, and Jacob was ok.

Where and when was this villain going to strike next I asked myself? *This is no good I thought, looking over my shoulder every two minutes, I had to get a grip and get on with things.*

We were racing that night at Mr Ryan's Downhill track with Lucky, it was his first open race at the track, he'd only run in graded races at the Ryan's, never in an open 450 yards.

Unaware to the other punters he'd won three races at other tracks. Billy had stayed at the kennels all day in case we might have had an unwanted visit. This was a race we'd been looking forward to for some time.

Lucky had come on in leaps and bounds and had the makings of a top class dog, the older he got the stronger he became. I'd saved a few quid as had Billy, Jimmy the beard and JW. *(Open race) any dog from anywhere can enter for this type of race).*

This was a real test for Lucky, the prize money was a respectable £80 for the winner and that meant there would be some good class dogs from all over the place. I was still confident Lucky could win, but if he was to be beaten by a better dog and did his best, that's all I could ask for.

Jill had made tea late that night at about 5-30, she needn't have bothered, for no one had any appetite, that is all except our youngest, he could eat a scabby cat could that boy. This put Jill in a right bad mood, she was annoyed that she'd cooked tea and none of the kids wanted any.

"If you kids *dare* ask for anything tu eat up at that track, I'll-- I'll, well yer know what tu expect, I've slaved on making yer tea's and it's been a complete waste of time."

When Jill lost her temper it was time to keep out of her way and say nothing---big mistake from little Paul. "I've eaten all my tea mam, I'll get something at the track won't ah."

"Yes yer bloody well will if yer ask son, try that for size," as she gave him a clip round the ear, then immediately grabbed hold of him to give him a hug, tears rolling down her face. That was completely out of character for Jill, the only thing you could put it down too was the events of the last couple of days.

Jill never smacked the kids, a pointed finger and a stern word generally did the trick. "Why is mummy crying dad," said Paul. *"It didn't even hurt us when me mam clipped us,"* he continued, sticking out his chest as he walked over to the other boys. Colin the oldest handed his mum a handkerchief that must have been in his pocket for God knows how long.

"Get yer coats on yer scamps or we are going to be late for the dogs." The kids made one mad dash for the coat cupboard all trying to get through the door together.

We started loading the van with the essentials for Lucky, hot water for his feet, drinking water and towels. The house door was locked and there was no going back in, this was an old superstition that we had carried on for as long as I can remember, if you lock the door and forget something, tough, you had to do without.

Billy arrived from the kennels with Lucky who looked a picture. "Put him into the van Bill everything else is in there ready." We were just about to set off when little Paul shouted out.

"Mam, a have tu go."

"What du yer mean, yer have tu go, you pick the finest times so yer do, why didn't yer go before we came out," asked Jill.

"Ah didn't want tu go then---but ah do now."

"Get one in the drain and hurry up," I shouted.

"But dad," said Paul holding onto his trousers.

"Never mind but Dad, there's nobody watching, get one in the bloody drain and hurry up about it." Paul scurried back down the yard to the drain on the corner of the house; he must have been there four or five minutes before Jill shouted to see if he was alright.

"Are yer finished yet Paul?" "Just about Mam but ah need some *paper!*"

The conversation stopped---everyone looked at each other shaking their heads in disbelief, a voice from down the yard calling, "It's alright mam, av'e got a sweet packet in me pocket, that'll do." Jill and I looked at each other and came out with the same words. *"Where the hell did we get him from?"*

"It's no good Tom, superstition or not, I can't leave *that* in the drain, plus the scruffy little toad wants his hands washed."

"Ah don't mam, because it was a big sweetie bag and ah didn't get anything on me hands, so it's ok."

Jill unlocked the door, filled a bucket of water and flushed the drain while Paul washed his hands insisting that they were clean owing to the size of the sweet bag. "Get in that van little un and move nothing but yer eyelids." *A horrible thought came into my head that this was not going to be our night.*

Thank the Lord we arrived at the track without further incident, Paul was on his best behaviour and Lucky taking it all in his stride like a veteran. I was just about to sort out the money for a bet with the lads when who should be walking towards me, none other than Stringvest and Annie, Jill and I hadn't seen the pair of them since that fiasco over the £5 note.

"Now Tom, Jill, lads, how's things," said Willie smartly dressed in a suit two sizes too big for him, both sleeves and trouser legs turned up several times, with a pair of braces over his stringvest pulling the waistband of the trousers nearly up to his armpits. Paul stood there looking up and down at Willie wondering why someone should be dressed like that.

"Fancy a drink lads," said Willie, "Am paying." "Yer must have come intu some money," said Jimmy. "Or you've nicked it from the same feller yer got that suit off."

"For your information whiskers, the suit was a gift from Annie, true it might be a little roomy, but that's just the way ah happen tu like me suits, and before yer ask it belonged to Annie's ex, he, er, left it when him and her had words," said Willie.

84

"Yer want tu hope he doesn't come looking for it," said Billy.

"Because the man that fits into that suit is some size Willie and if he wants it back, he's going tu kick seven sorts of shsss er sawdust out of yer." Jill gave Billy the evil eye before he finished his sentence.

"Can der owners of dogs in der open race please come tu der paddock tu draw for traps tank you." Mr Ryan was as broad an Irishman as you could get and at times it was a little difficult to understand the old gent, but we always got there in the end.

We walked round to the paddock where Billy was waiting to draw for traps, I wasn't to worried about what number we drew as Lucky had won three races all from different traps.

Mr Ryan held up his cap containing the six numbers. "Lady's first if yer please," said the old Irishman. A rather large lady stepped forward to draw for Sinbad, a blonde brassy type, thick red lipstick and enough jewellery to set up her own shop, she waddled over to Mr Ryan, all 16 to 17 stone of her and dipped her hand into the cap pulling out the white ball. Billy quickly moved Lucky to one side well out of danger of being stepped on.

"Number tree will be Sinbad," shouted Mr Ryan.

"Next tu draw is Toby." A thin man dipped his hand into the cap and pulled out number four the black trap.

"Could we have der owner of Molly tu draw for traps please." A tall six foot character stepped forward, cap pulled well down over his face, his blonde hair showing down the back of his neck. This was obviously, someone trying to keep his identity well under raps, probably from one of the licensed tracks who are not allowed to take part at any flapping establishments.

85

"Molly draws trap one the red trap, next to draw is Rustick," shouted Mr Ryan. Then a man holding a small boy in his arms lifted him up to place his hand into the cap. "Pull the number out of the hat son, lets see what we have." "Rustic draws trap five, just two numbers left."

"Right Bill," said Mr Ryan, "Will yer putting in yer hand and pulling out a number for your dog Echo." Billy pulled out the blue ball, number two.

We were just about to leave the paddock when someone from the crowd shouted. "There are only five dogs." Sure enough there were only five dogs.

"Be Jesus dats right so it is and me not even noticing a dog missing," he had a quick glance at his notepad to discover the missing dogs name was Just Black and was about to call it a none runner when a young man dashed into the paddock. "Sorry Mr, van, brock darn." His accent was recognised and unmistakeable. I had spent several good years working in the pits in Yorkshire and found the people both helpful and friendly. "Tings like dat happen son, haven't we all been in dat em predicumnment if dats der word I'm er looking for."

"It's *predicament* yer old fool and dats what you'll be in if yer don't get dis race off soon," said Mrs Ryan, standing in the paddock tapping her foot impatiently at the delay.

"Don't you be telling me my job yer old crone," said Mr Ryan pointing a finger at his wife. I'd seen this sort of thing with the Ryan's go on for any length of time and feared the worst.

Young Patrick the eldest of the Ryan's decided to take charge and asked the owners of the dogs to take them to the traps. Mr and Mrs Ryan were still arguing and not taking a blind bit of notice of the dogs leaving the paddock.

86

There was only one dog left, the late arrival Just Black. The young man took off the black dogs walking out coat and put on the black and white striped racing jacket, number six.

Billy being curious and nosey manoeuvred himself to stand next to the latecomer with Lucky alongside, you could hardly split the pair. The height looks and condition of the two dogs were nearly identical. By this time the Ryan's had sorted themselves out and were scurrying to their posts. Jimmy JW and myself made our way down to the bookies.

"Two to one the field," shouted fat Ronnie with his unmistakable rosy cheeks and fat jowls. One of the owners of the dogs in the race must have really fancied his chances as he took the 2/1 for Toby the four dog.

That set the ball rolling for the rest of the betting as the other dogs went out in price. "Three to one Just Black, Echo and Molly, four to one Sinbad and Rustick," shouted fat Ronnie as he stuffed the money into his satchel. Jill and the kids were holding back with their bets on the tote to couple Lucky, (Echo) with one or two of their own fancies for the forecast, first or second in any order.

"Two minutes lady's and gents, two minutes left," came the announcement. More panic from one or two of the remaining owners. Jimmy, JW and myself were holding on until the time was right to bet Lucky.

Crash went fat Ronnie's beer crate he was standing on as he was toppled to the ground as the crowd surged forward with their bets.

"Grab that bloody satchel Flash," he shouted to his clerk as he struggled to lift his large frame upright.

Time was running out, the announcement came to place the dogs into the traps. This was it, I gave the signal to Jimmy and JW to move in and place their bets, quick as a flash and the business was done at 4/1.

Fat Ronnie was still dusting himself off after his crashing fall, but still managed to take on all comers.

Every dog in the race had been backed, or so we thought! Right at the very last second the bookmakers were bombarded with a load of money for Just Black, the six dog.

Whoever owned this dog must have had an immense amount of faith in his animal, or too much money, either way we were about to find out.

The hare was in motion and coming up to the traps, swish as it flashed past the traps and the dogs were released, from what I could see Lucky had started well from trap two--- but not as well as trap six. There were three lengths between them at the first bend. I could hear Jill and the kids screaming at the top of their voices.

"Come on Lucky, you can do it," they screamed, but by the time they were at the last bend I could see Lucky was beat.

"First number six Just Black, second number two Echo, der winning time, now let me see, ah yes, we have a new track record of 26-18, der winner won by two and a half lengths beating de old record of 26-30, now isn't dat grand so it is." Mr Ryan was pleased that a dog had broken the track record, it showed that his track was running well and that would attract the punters and the good dogs back to the track.

Billy walked off the track, a look of disappointment etched on his rugged face but still had time to offer his hand to the boy leading off the winner, the boy walked straight past as if Billy wasn't there.

"Could we be having der young feller and his dog Just Black, tu der paddock tu receive his prize money please."

The boy headed towards the paddock, took the envelope from Mr Ryan then walked straight out of the gate without saying a word to anyone.

There was a look of amazement on the old gents face as he stood there with his hand still held out to congratulate the young man. Jill and the kids had made their way round to where we were standing. I caught hold of Colin our oldest boy and instructed him to follow the boy with the winner.

Meantime Jimmy, JW and myself had the gut wrenching job of paying our money over to the bookies, not a nice feeling and one I hoped I wasn't going to get into a habit of.

Jill and the kids had gone out of the track ready to meet Lucky, win draw or lose there was always a greeting for whatever dog we had run.

I handed my money to fat Ronnie who was gathering his cash by the handful from his over laden satchel.

"Good result Ron," I asked as he folded the notes into one hundred pound bundles. "Not really Tom, it might have been if there hadn't been a last minute job for that bastard winner, took a bloody fortune out of the bag the useless bass," he was just about to finish off his word when he caught sight of our Collin running full pelt towards me.

"Dad," he puffed, standing with his hands on his knees trying to compose himself.

"Take yer time son, they've probably long gone by now anyway."

"Yer right dad, he puffed, they were parked right at the top of the car park, a little white van and the driver was ready to set off because the lad just had time to shove the dog in the back door and they were gone, didn't even give the dog a drink, or wash his feet."

"Well done son, yer did a good job, not that it makes us any wiser at the moment."

It had to be someone with something to hide, or wanting to keep a low profile---that pointed to a licensed trainer. Only time would tell, but one thing was for sure, I didn't want to meet that dog again.

Billy had taken Lucky to the van where Jill and the kids were waiting to smother him with kisses and hugs. "Wait a minute kids, feet washed then a good drink before anything else." No matter where any of the dogs finished they all got the same treatment, including the kisses.

Billy left Lucky in the van with Jill and the kids; just for safekeeping, after all we still had to be on our toes after that Herman incident.

Jimmy and JW were paying their losing bets to the bookies when the team that backed Just Black came to collect their winnings. JW and the Beard stood their ground in front of the books until the strangers handed in their tickets, they hoped to pick up any clues as to where the dog or it's backers came from.

Each one of the men handed in his ticket at the same time, not a word was spoken and all drew the same amount of money £1,500 each, they'd all had £300 on at 4-1, plus their stake.

They were walking away counting their money when one of the gang stopped; a shifty looking character heavily tattooed on his fingers with the words love on one hand and hate on the other.

He turned to the bookmaker he had won the money from, Slippery Sam, aptly named, he'd rob his own mother if he could get away with it. "Thar's med a mistake pal," said the well built man staring straight into the eye's of Sam and holding out his winnings to be re-counted.

"Er what mistake would that be bonny lad," said Sam shrugging his shoulders and holding out his arms trying to indicate that all was well.

"A fifty quid mistake," said the man with a real menacing look. "And I ain't a bonny lad mister as thar's about tu find out if ah dun't get me money thar owes me." The man's strong Yorkshire accent distinctive for all to hear, Billy had made his way back into the track just in time to see the trouble erupting. Sam looked at the notes held out by the man demanding they be counted again.

"The money was right when yer left here son." Sam had hardly got the word son, from his mouth before the man had him by the throat with one hand and his clerk with the other.

"Thar better count me fifty quid from that there money bag pal before this grip gets any tighter," he said to the shaking clerk. "Or thee mate here, will be having difficulty counting at all."

The petrified clerk quickly counted out the money, the stranger with a steel like grip on Sam's throat who was by this time gasping for air. The man's mates closed in menacingly.

"Thee fatty," said the man pointing to fat Ronnie who was standing by watching the event. Ronnie in turn pointing to himself. "I thee," said the man. "Count that bundle of notes, thar'll see there's only £1,450 plus that £50 what that old git tried tu rob me of, when thar's done that I'm gunna let this bag of shit loose-- if he goes for coppers or track owner, am gunner come back for *thee*, ok suthee," a familiar Yorkshire word. After the re-count the man and his mates made their way out of the track.

By this time Mr Ryan had arrived to see why the crowd was gathering around the bookmakers. He pushed his way through to the front, all eight stone of him, demanding to know what the problem was.

Slippery Sam was sitting on his beer crate recovering, beads of sweat running down his face as he struggled to undo his tie so he could breath more easily.

"Be Jesus Sam, would yer be havin a problem there, yer sitting der sweating like a man who's just been caught by yer girlfriends husband wit yer trousers down so yer have ha, ha." Laughing at his own joke, Mr Ryan looked round for a response from the crowd and getting none.

There was no reply from Sam, or anyone else if it came to that. Seeing the actions of the Yorkshire lad and what his mates were capable of was enough to silence most people.

From what I had seen of the race, a better dog had beaten Lucky. Billy assured me that our dog was sound and therefore there were no excuses.

We discussed the race at length and came to the conclusion that Just Black was a dog from one of the licensed tracks, hence the secrecy and quick getaway.

"There's always another day Tom," said Jimmy rubbing the top of my head. "Lucky's a good dog and we won't be dropping on a Just Black every time we race, or will we?"

I had a gut feeling that Jimmy was wrong and we would be having more than one encounter with Just Black.

Two weeks had gone by, Lucky's defeat had been forgotten and there had been no more sightings or rumours of Herman. I felt very uneasy; this wasn't like a man that thrived on revenge. His humiliation that day at Jacob's shop would be avenged at some time, but where, when and how, was the question.

Jill and I had decided to have a night out with the kids at the local fair, not my cup of tea and the kids knew this. I'd rather give them all a few bob to spend on anything rather than the fair. As we strolled round, the lights were flashing, the sirens blasting and the kids pulling at our arms wanting to ride on everything that moved, from the big dipper to the helter-skelter. We had just got to the dodgems when we bumped into Brendan and Maxine.

Brendan loved kids and in no time at all he had plunged his hand in his pocket rummaging about for change.

"Here yer go kids, der's two shilling's each and don't be taken any notice of yer father, I've known him a long time so ah have and ah know how he feels about spending money at der fair, so scoot off before he has time tu tink about what tu do tu try an stop yer, go on scoot, quick."

I was just about to give Brendan a good ticking off, when Jill gave me one of her puppy-eyed looks. That was enough for me, plus Brendan was too bloody big to argue with.

The kids scattered before anyone could say anything, Jill shouted to Colin to keep an eye on them especially with the Herman situation.

Brendan apologised for giving the kids the money, then retracted it saying "I'm not sorry really Tom," with a smile from ear to ear. "While we are on the apologies lark Brendan, what happened two weeks ago when yer were supposed tu meet me at the track when Lucky was running?" A red-faced Brendan looked over to Maxine.

"Well, it was like dis Tom so it was." Maxine glared at Brendan who was struggling to find an excuse.

93

"It was der truck Tom so it was, bloody puncture, no time tu fix it." "No puncture Tom," interrupted Maxine. "Dat tick head forgot half der shopping after dat little escapade wit dem tree fellers, so we had tu go shopping in der next village, by der time we got home and fixed a meal it was too late."

"But der meal was nice Max so it was," said Brendan trying to get off the subject.

"Talking about fights," said the big feller. "I'm feeling a bit lucky so I am, der's £5 tu der man dat can last tree rounds wit der champ in dat der booth, be Jesus am having some of dat so I am."

Maxine and Brendan had brought their pet dog Heinz, a suitable name considering the mixture of breeds he was. Long ears, short tail, squashed up face, big feet, long hair and a mixture of colours, a description that could match the fast approaching Stringvest walking towards us. "Tom, Jill, Max, Brendan, how's thing's." "Not bad Willie, where's Annie," I asked.

"She's er treating the kids on the shows Tom, we bumped intu your Collin on the dodgems the kids are having a cracking time."

Brendan started shadow boxing and was itching to get into the fighting booth before it closed.

"Would yer be doing me a favour Willie," taking the lead from Maxine and shoving it towards Willie's hand. "Keep hold of dat old dog for me." Before Willie could give Brendan an answer the dog lead was in his hand and Brendan and Max were heading for the booth.

"But, but." "Don't keep doing that Willie yer sound like Mrs Moffit at the Chippy," said Jill as we followed Brendan and Max into the booth.

"Ask Annie tu look after the kids Willie, we won't be long--- that's if Brendan's on form," shouted Jill.

Willie stood there, mouth wide open scratching his head wondering how he'd been left on his own holding the dog. He'd been standing there for about fifteen to twenty minutes, when four troublesome looking youths approached him, all looking a little worse for wear through the drink.

"That's the ugliest dog av ever seen in me life," slurred the tallest of the four. "Yer reet," agreed one of his mates teasing the dog with his foot. "Does---- yer-- dog bite mister," slurred one of the four.

"Nor bonny lad, me dog doesn't bite, quiet as a mouse my dog." The tallest youth leaned forward to touch Heinz when the dog grabbed hold of his hand sinking its teeth into his flesh.

"Wow yer bastard," he screamed, as the other lads stood back in shock. "He's drawn blood Smithy look," shouted the youth screaming in agony, "That bloody dogs dangerous mate, should be put down and you yer little fat toad, yer said yer dog didn't bite." "Yer reet bonny lad," said Willie. "Ah *did* say me dog didn't bite, *but this isn't my dog.*" One of the lads was just about to have a kick at Heinz when Willie pointed at Brendan coming from the fighting booth looking unscathed. *"It's his dog."* The youth's took one look at Brendan counting out his money from his presumed victory and scarpered quickly. Brendan all smiles shoved a fiver into Willie's hand.

"Dat's fer yer trouble Willie," "No trouble at all Brendan, the dogs been like an old lamb not a hapeth of bother," said Willie with a wink and a shake of his head. The kids came back all smiles with Annie, after having a good time, carrying

95

candyfloss and toffee apples. Young Paul was looking especially pleased with himself as he held onto his goldfish in his see-through bag. The prize had been won by our Colin for knocking down all the empty cans. Jill and I had also won a few bob on Brendan fighting, all in all it was a real good night.

CHAPTER TWELVE

It was time for Lucky's next race; we'd decided to run him at Ships End track in a small open race, just to give him a confidence booster after his defeat in his last race. I wanted to assure myself that he was as good as I thought he was.

We were in the sixth race, we arrived at the track just that little bit early but with good reason. I didn't want to have another encounter with *Just Black*, the dog that had beaten him in his last race.

Jill sat with Lucky in the van knitting away quietly. Our kids had more woolly scarves and gloves than any other kids in the North East.

Billy, Jim, JW and myself were sitting on the small wall about twenty yards from the paddock when we saw Cautious Mervin, you know the type, looks both ways on a one way street.

Mervin would check every little thing daily, oil and water for the car, the pressure in the tyres, he'd leave the house then go back just to make sure he'd locked the door, Mervin was ultra cautious.

After placing his dog Pit Lamp into the kennels, he sat on the wall opposite. Mervin was only about five yards from myself and the rest of the lads, I gave Jimmy a nudge and a wink.

"Somebody told me that there's been one or two dogs got at in the kennels lately." I was speaking just loud enough for Cautious to creek his head in our direction. Billy echoed my words saying he'd heard the same rumour. Then JW Chipped in.

"Apparently the gang fix a piece of doped meat on the cross frame of the inner door, when the door of the kennel is slammed shut, the doped meat falls off into the straw bedding and the dog gets stuck in, sweet dreams for the dog."

JW had hardly got the words from his mouth when Cautious was off the wall like a sprinter, unlocking the kennel with great speed. The dog was so keen to be out of the kennel thinking it was time for his race that he knocked poor Cautious over.

After tying the dog to a post he frantically pulled out every bit of straw he could find until the kennel was completely empty. Covered from head to toe in bits of chaff, he then started on the door, inch by inch and then the wooden bench the dog had been resting on. Every square inch in that kennel was thoroughly examined.

We were doubled up with laughter watching his antics, at one time I thought he was going to ask if anyone had a screwdriver, he did everything but take the kennel door off its hinges.

Cautious looked a right wally on all four's checking every bit of straw for traces of anything that didn't look right. In the end he gave up, kicked the straw to one side and placed his coat on the bench for the dog to lie down on muttering to himself as he left the paddock. "You can't be to careful, you just can't be to careful," he muttered.

Suddenly Cautious hesitated and looked back, we thought hi up, he's going through it all again, but he didn't, he just sat down on the wall, poking his finger down his ear, shaking his head where some of the chaff must have started to annoy him.

God only knows what was going on in that mind of his.

The runners were called for the third race, three more races to go before Lucky's race. It would take that amount of time for me and the lads to calm down, I hadn't laughed like that in a long time and to be honest, it might have been a bit cruel but it did me the world of good.

The next two races passed and still no sign of the Yorkshire lads or *Just black*. Jill could hear the announcement for the dogs in the open race as she sat in the van still passing the time knitting.

The lads and myself were gathered round the paddock half hoping *Just Black* would not be in the race. *Then I thought to myself, what the hell, we can't avoid this dog forever. Who knows, we might beat him next time we meet.*

There were three dogs on parade in the paddock, one fawn, one black and white, and one all black. Definitely not the dog we were looking for, this black dog had too much white on his feet.

Jill arrived with Lucky, who was looking a picture, standing there wearing his new walking out coat that Jacob had made and generously given us. Lucky was the only dog in the paddock to have a coat on, that was one thing that I'd learned from an early age you must keep your dog warm.

My grandfather would say, you never see an athlete take his tracksuit off until the last minute, it's the same with a dog, keep him warm.

The handicapper entered the paddock and asked the owners for the names of their dogs. As they were shouted out he ticked them off accordingly.

We had decided to call Lucky by another name, Sooty. The other dogs were, Minty, Toffee and Drummer. Still two more

99

entries to check in. "Can we have Popcorn and Yorkshire Lad tu the Paddock," shouted the handicapper, a stout man, his hair what there was of it, four or five strands combed to one side.

A smart young lady entered the paddock being pulled by a powerful brindle dog. "I'm terribly sorry I'm a bit late, car trouble," she said.

"That's alright bonny lass, next time get a better car, or set off a bit earlier ok, what's the dogs name pet we're running a bit late." "Popcorn," she replied. This handicapper always had an answer for everyone no matter who they were.

Just then the last dog and his handler came walking into the paddock, a smart looking black dog, well coated up.

"Is this Yorkshire Lad," asked the handicapper.

"Ah that's reet," replied the handler. "Yer late, yer must have walked it from Yorkshire son, next time get a lift," said the handicapper in his usual sarcastic way, a chuckle from the crowd put a smile on the young mans face.

Before the man could answer, Jill was asked to draw for traps, as she was the first lady into the paddock. She placed her hand into the cap and drew out the blue ball, number two. "Sooty draws trap two," shouted the handicapper showing the blue ball to the crowd. We were happy enough with our draw.

My eyes hadn't left the dog called Yorkshire Lad; there was every possibility that this could be Just Black. "Right," shouted the handicapper, "Next tu draw will be Popcorn," the young lady placed her hand into the cap and drew out number four, the black jacket. Minty drew the red trap number one and Toffee drew number three, the white jacket.

"Right lads, that just leaves Drummer and our friend from

Yorkshire tu draw for traps." The owner of Drummer drew five the orange jacket. That just left trap six the striped Jacket. "It dun't mek any difference tu me Mr, this feller comes out of any box, no problem at all," said the cocky young chap with Yorkshire Lad, looking quite confident as he picked up the striped jacket.

This meant the dog could be good and possibly Just Black, or just another good dog. We were about to find out as the walking out coat came off. The wise lads in the crowd had their minds made up before the coat came off that this was Just Black.

I was certain it wasn't the same dog. I'd had a good look at it the night we were beaten and made sure that I'd recognise him if we ever met again. Just Black and Lucky were very similar, as close as you'd get for a pair of ringers---apart from two things.

Every dog has a mole or two on his face; Just Black had the same amount of moles as Lucky, two. But one of the moles on Just Black's face had two hairs, and only one sticking out from the other mole, plus he had a white toenail amongst the black ones on his back inside leg. Lucky had just the one hair sticking out from each mole and no white toenails at all.

From the position I was standing in the paddock I could easily see that Yorkshire Lad had just the one mole and three white nails on his back inside leg, therefore he couldn't be Just Black. That was good enough for me.

This meant the punters would make Yorkshire Lad favourite and also gave me the confidence to have a good bet on Lucky. I told Billy and the lads that the black dog was not the dog everyone thought it was and that was good enough for them. We pooled our money together, making £420, my £200 and the rest between the lads.

Just as we thought, the punters had made Yorkshire Lad favourite at 6/4. Lucky was 5/2. A sudden rush of money for Toffee the three dog forced the favourite out to 2/1 and Lucky out to 3/1. The punters were totally convinced that the favourite was the dog that had broken the track record at Downhill track as they steamed in again knocking the price down to even money.

The announcement came to put the dogs into the traps, the hare was running when I gave the nod to the lads to back Lucky (Sooty) his price had gone out to 4/1. The hare flashed past the traps, Lucky was out like a bat out of hell and round the first bend like a flash, I could hear Jill and the kids screaming encouragement at the top of their voices.

There was no need Lucky had won comfortably. This was a great result after the disappointment at the Downhill track; the money I'd won would also come in handy for Jill and the kids, it was badly needed after Lucky's last defeat.

"Result of the sixth race, the open, first number two Sooty, second number five Drummer, distance four and a half lengths and the winning time 28-30." This was just two lengths short of the track record and a cracking run from Lucky who was running over the 500 yards for the first time.

We drew our money from the bookies and for once they were pleased to be paying out. The amount of money that had gone on the Yorkshire dog must have been substantial for the books to be paying out with a smile. Nobody had a bigger smile than Jill.

The kids were all over Lucky when Jill brought him off the track hugging and kissing him, mind you I don't know who was doing the most kissing, Lucky or Paul, as the youngster had just finished off a meat pie and had more on his face than anywhere else. With the excitement of the race he'd missed his mouth and that was very unusual for Paul, mind you I don't think Lucky was complaining.

We were just about to go to the judge's box for the prize money when the handicapper himself came walking towards us. "Nice dog young Watson, ran well, is he for sale" he asked. "Not really," I replied and held out my hand for the prize money. This was a man I just couldn't get on with, he could pull all the strokes he liked on other tracks by running his own dogs and sending them in with other people, but didn't like the same done to him at his track. "Yer sure yer don't want ter sell that dog Watson," he asked again as he counted out the prize money into my hand. "I'm as sure as I've just won that race," I said. "Anyway Watson, what's the reason yer haven't been entering yer dogs on the card."

"That's easy Benny---yer never give them a chance."

"Rubbish," replied the handicapper.

"Put one of your dogs on for Tuesday and see what chance yer get." This was sounding to good to be true and I started to smell a rat, as did the rest of the lads. So I thought to myself, play the man at his own game and lets see what happens.

"Right Benny, put Scarface on in a sprint."

"Champion he's on for Tuesday," said the wise cracking handicapper as he walked off to prepare for the next race.

Scarface had run at Benny's track on numerous occasions and never had a chance to win a race. It would be interesting to see just what the man was up to. Billy, Jim and JW were all against running the old dog. Jill didn't look overjoyed at the idea either. We found out later that night that Benny was short of dogs and was struggling to make out a full race card. The man had offended so many people over the years that they were taking their dogs elsewhere to race and who could blame them.

We'd had a really good night, Lucky was sound, we'd all won a few quid and as usual we ended up at Mrs Moffits fish shop. She looked troubled and didn't seem to be her usual joyful self for some reason. We ordered our fish and chip lots as we always did when we'd had a winner. Mrs Moffit didn't say a word. Jill had given the kids their lots and left the shop, leaving me to pay the old lady. I was counting out the money onto the counter when Mrs Moffit grabbed my hand.

"Ttttom,"she stuttered."Ah diidaant wwant tu say anything wwhen JJjill wwas tthere." "Say what Mrs Moffit," I interrupted. "Ah hhad aa cuustermer in tunnight wwwho tells me Heerman ppassed through thhe viilage inn aah bbig fflassh ccar, wwhach wwhat yer ddoing Tttom."

I thanked the old lady and left the shop. Jill was standing there tapping her foot waiting and giving me the evil look.

"What the hell took yer sur long, suppers gunna be frozen," she said, her foot tapping faster.

"Jill yer know what Mrs Moffits like when she starts stuttering, it takes her all day tu say just a few words, the woman can't help it."

"Yer right Tom, she's a good old soul really, ah shouldn't be mad she's been a good friend tu us over the years, anyway what was she talking about?" "Ah yer know, the price of fish, what else." I didn't dare tell Jill that Herman was back, just when things were starting to pick up. I decided to let Billy and the lads know to keep them on their toes, we all agreed to get on with things the best way we could and take it day by day.

Tuesday morning, after walking out the dogs and seeing to their breakfast I called in to see old Jacob, just to make sure he hadn't had a visit from our old enemy.

I'd never seen him happier. "Tom my boy how nice to see you, how are the little ones and of course your good lady, you need something Tom, is that why you have called into my shop, you can have what you want my friend."

It was obvious the old man had not had a visit from our old enemy and that could only be good for the both of us. "Just called in Jacob to see how things are with you and pick up a paper from the paper shop, but I can see yer fine Jacob and I must get back, still plenty of work tu be done when you've got dogs tu keep." Happy that Jacob was alright, I was keen to get back home to Jill and the kids.

The smell of cooked bacon greeted me as I entered the house; there was nothing like a good fry up tu get your morning going. Billy and Jimmy had helped up at the kennels and that gave Jill time tu see the kids off tu School.

If Herman was up tu no good I couldn't see him doing anything in front of hundreds of school kids, besides there was always a copper on the corner watching the little un's over the road.

After breakfast I checked the paper tu see if Benny the handicapper had kept his word and given the old dog Scarface a chance. The mark he'd given the dog was to good to be true. He was receiving four yards start in a sprint and that was a brilliant mark.

I knew every dog in the race and we had the beating of them all. But why the big chance I asked myself. I met Billy and the lads back at the kennels late morning to discuss the situation.

105

We were all agreed, there had tu be a rabbit off and not the one on the track!

We met back at our house later that afternoon before going to the track, I'd kept the old dog in a kennel we had at home. (Scarface) his pet name was Champ, I'd rescued him from a villain that was going to have him put to sleep over a year ago and he'd been with us ever since.

I decided to let old Champ have his head and run, but with a great deal of caution. There had to be a reason why the handicapper had given the old dog a chance. I'd rather trust a rattlesnake than that man, we just didn't see eye to eye.

We arrived at the track a little bit early just to see if there was anything unusual, like a cut up race, (where all the owners of a race get their heads together and bet just one dog) or perhaps a ringing job, (not the right dog). I'd spoken to one or two of the regulars and the only thing I could get from them was that Champ was a good thing, but his price would be very short odds in the betting.

Billy, Jim and JW had decided to have a £100 bet between them, but only if Champ was even money or better. Two more races before Champ's race and I still had this gut feeling that something was wrong.

An old mate of mine who I hadn't seen for a while came over for a word, a grin from ear to ear. Tommy the cap was his name, slightly built, horn-rimmed glasses and a cheese cutter cap. "How's thing going Tom," he asked, shaking my hand vigorously. "So so Tommy," I replied not wanting to go into detail about Herman.

"How's things with you Tommy," I asked, "Wife and kids ok." He hesitated with his answer. "Things would be a lot better Tom if me luck would change, if ah didn't have bad luck ad hev none at all." Tommy was a good lad with a nice wife and two good sons, if he could help you in any way he wouldn't hesitate to do so.

The announcement came over the crackly old loudspeaker for the runners in Champ's race. I made my way over to the paddock, Tommy the cap not far behind me. Billy, Jimmy and JW were already there looking at the opposition.

No ringers and no dogs looking the worse for wear amongst the dogs that were in the paddock. Only one more dog to be declared to make the race complete---An announcement crackled over the old speaker. "Number three in this race is a none runner, the reserve Happy Jenny runs from five yards."

I asked one of the locals, old Hayden who never missed a meeting how the bitch had been running, "Been in season bonny lad, Benny the handicapper's had it kennelled at the track for the last ten weeks, the lad who owns her, Ginger O'Donnel has been working away on the pipeline, never seen him for ah don't know how long."

Things didn't seem right, this was an untrusting handicapper and something smelled, the only thing to do was wait for the betting. We had all decided not to bet Champ, unless there was no money for the rest of the dogs in the race.

"Even money for this good thing," shouted Butch the bookie a fat greasy tub of lard with unkempt hair and an odour as bad as a skunk, not to mention his breath. "Come on you punters, they're going into the traps, even money Scarface yer better get on before it's too late." Tommy the cap whispered into my ear to put him £40 on Champ if we were going to bet on him, I looked him in the eye and nodded.

"Put them dogs in the traps Mr starter," came the announce-.

ment. Butch shouted out "2/1 Scarface," the locals nearly knocked him off his beer crate.

The other five bookies still had Champ at even money, the rest of the field were three's and four's with Happy Jenny 5/1. Tommy was eager to bet Champ at 2/1 and asked why the delay.

"Champ can't get beat Tom, yer not gunner get a better price than that," he whispered. He'd hardly got the words from his mouth when a team of complete strangers rushed into the other five bookmakers and backed Happy Jenny off the boards, not a price of any description left.

Up went the traps, out came Jenny with our dog Champ three lengths behind and that's the way the race finished. Either Jenny *was* a ringer, or she had found a new lease of life.

We had very nearly been caught, unfortunately the only people that had been hurt were the local punters and the bookies, that is all but Butch the handicapper's relation. The handicapper had placed old Scarface in the race to make a better price for Happy Jenny to try and catch the lads and myself--- but it didn't work. Tommy the cap could not have been more relieved. "Tom that was me last forty quid, if ad lost that the wife would have killed me, a owe yer big time Tom and if ah can do anything for yer, consider it's done."

Maybe Tommy's luck had started to change for the better after all. Jill came off the track to the usual greeting from the kids with hugs and kisses for old Champ. The handicapper had played his ace and caught all but one of the bookies. As for the punters, there's an old saying in the dog game, you pay yer money and you take yer chance. I was lucky and hadn't fallen into the trap. A valuable lesson had been learned. If there was anything I hated more than Herman, it was someone as devious and as arrogant as Mr Benny Martin. I knew my patience with this handicapper some day would pay off and that my time would come to get even.

CHAPTER THIRTEEN

IT was Anytime Annie's birthday, Stringvest Willie her on/off boyfriend had decided to treat her to a little party down at the Pig and Whistle. We were all invited, myself, Jill, Brendan and Maxine.

Annie sat there downing drink after drink, Maxine doing likewise with her favourite tipple whisky. Simon, the landlord was working overtime trying to keep up with the demand, a rare smile on his face for a change. Willie had paid for a sit down meal and to my surprise it looked really good. There were chicken legs, beef, chips, pork pies and a variety of other foods.

Simon had shoved five tables together. Willie at one end, Annie at the other. He'd also done well with the food and that was evident when you looked at Willie's face. You'd have thought Annie had been feeding him with a catapult from the other end of the table. Gravy down his chin, cream on the end of his nose and various bits of food dotted here and there about his face.

Things were going well, everyone was having a good time laughing, singing and dancing, when the sound of crockery falling onto the floor startled everyone. The noise came from the direction of the kitchen.

Simon walked into the bar looking like he'd seen a ghost.

The whole pub went deathly silent--- that is all but Brendan and Willie. "Are we in der right pub Simon," asked Brendan, "Because ah tort der Greeks were der one's dat

110

broke all der plates so ah did." The silence in the room was only broken by Willie breaking wind and receiving a clip across the ear from Annie who had ventured from the other end of the table to give Willie a much needed napkin.

Simon looked visibly shaken; I took him to one side and tried to ease him towards the kitchen to check the damage, his feet not wanting to move.

"Come on bonny lad things canner be that bad man, it's only a few broken plates." I tried once more to move him in the direction of the kitchen; he was having none of it.

"Don't go in there Tom, just--- don't," he repeated as he stood there ridged, fear etched on his chalk white face.

I left Simon and went into the kitchen despite his protests---nothing in here but a load of broken plates I said to myself. "Simon," I shouted, "What's the problem, so you've broken a few plates so what." Simon moved steadily into the kitchen ignoring the broken plates on the floor, looking around as if he was expecting someone to jump out.

When we returned to the bar, Willie, well gone with the drink slurred--- "Yer er want tu stop drinking that stuff yer selling Simon, it hic does funny er things tu yer mind, ah mean look what it's done tu Annie," his words not helped by another slap across the head by his girlfriend as she stood up to leave the room

Finally Simon shook his head and muttered to himself, "I must have been seeing things."

"Seeing what Simon, little green men or pink elephants, like Willie just said son, ease off the hard stuff."

"Tom, you've known me for a long time, long enough tu know that ah don't get drunk when am working, ah saw what ah saw." "What was that bonny lad?" No matter what Simon

111

had seen, or not seen, he didn't want to discuss it so I decided to let the matter drop, at least for the time being.

Willie, by this time had got himself into a right drunken stupor and challenged Brendan to an arm wrestling contest.

"Be Jesus Willie ah can beat yer meself never mind Brendan," said Maxine still knocking back the whiskies. This started a betting frenzy among the drinkers in the pub who would bet on anything and were always up for a laugh.

The table was cleared and the match was about to start when Maxine interrupted. "Ah need tu hold ontu me whisky wit me non-drinking hand so ah do, is der a problem wit dat Willie," she asked looking nearly as glossy eyed as her opponent. "No problem-- at all," slurred Willie. They grasped each others hand and took the strain, Willie sweating like a bull, Max keeping an eye on her non-drinking hand still holding a glass half full with whisky.

Harry the wig was to be the umpire; he had the worst wig that had ever been made, a bright ginger curly mass of hair. It just sat there like a cat on top of his head ready to pounce at any time.

I often wondered if someone were to put a saucer of milk down, would it jump straight from his head, or just sit there?

"On the count of three start the contest," shouted Harry. "One, two," Harry's wig slipped further and further over his eye's with each thump of his hand on the table. By the time he'd got to three the wig was on the floor and the room was in stitches.

Willie's veins bulged from his neck as he tried in vain to force Maxine's arm flat to the table. The sweat dripped from his forehead like a tap. Maxine's eye's were glued to her hand holding the whisky.

A slight vibration through the glass gave Maxine the strength she needed to overpower Willie and his hand crashed to the table; a great cheer went up from Maxine's supporters.

"Ah never thought yer could beat me Max," said Willie his eyes looking very glazed. "Don't tell--- Annie," he slurred, "Or al be in for another beating."

"Der was never any danger Willie me boy as long as ah had dat whisky in me hand, have yer ever---ever seen me spill a drop of der hard stuff, have yer ever now," she repeated, a groan came from a drunken Willie, now sprawled all over the table.

Annie had missed the excitement, walking back to the table after some considerable time outside. The noise was just dying down a little; there was a look of suspicion on one or two of the regulars face's that knew of Annie's reputation.

"What ---What the hell happened here," she asked, a look of innocence on her face, as she glanced down at a drunken boyfriend.

"If there's anything ah can't stand it's a man that can't hold his liquor," she said shaking her head in disgust.

A hush came over the room as a tall rough looking character appeared in the doorway, he looked round the room then walked towards the table where Annie had sat down next to her very drunken boyfriend. I'd seen this guy before, but I just couldn't think where, my mind was doing overtime trying to place him?

He looked down at Annie and asked her name. "What business is it of yours," she asked, shoving up what little bust she had with her arm, then turning her head to one side as she flicked up her dishevelled hair at the same time. "Because am asking," said the thug his tone of voice turned very aggressive.

"My friend, say's that your name is Annie, Anytime Annie, anywhere, and anyhow." He can vouch for your actions about half an hour ago now it's my turn." Annie turned and looked the man straight in the eye and said. "Ah don't know who you or your mate are, and to be honest ah don't care, as for what ah think yer asking me tu do, *I'd rather eat the balls off a skunk.*"

One or two of the regulars anticipated trouble and moved their seats back. That is all but Brendan and Willie, Willie incapable of moving anything. Brendan stood there stroking his chin as he stared at the thug who was shouting off his mouth.

I quickly stood up, my mind racing, I remembered where I'd seen the creep who was causing all the trouble, he was one of Herman's men that Brendan had punched outside of old Jacob's shop.

"Be Jesus it's just come tu me where av seen dat feller before, was he not der shit head who ran ontu me head dat time outside der old Jewish fellers place?"

Brendan had just confirmed my thoughts. The thug realised he'd had an unpleasant encounter with Brendan in the past and didn't fancy the same treatment so decided to kick over a few tables and chairs instead.

Simon watched from the end of the bar not saying a word, looking as white as a sheet. Why didn't he intervene, what was his problem?

The room went deathly quiet as three burly men walked in through the door, it was obvious for all to see, the problem was none other than the devil himself, *Herman.* Jill grabbed my arm as the three men walked over to where we were standing.

114

I gripped a Newcastle Brown Ale bottle firmly in my hand behind my back.

"Well, Well," said Herman a snigger coming from that evil face of his.

"What a nice little gathering have we got here--- Mr Watson who can't mind his own business, Anytime Annie who can't seem tu get enough---- er business and then there's that excuse for a boyfriend Stringvest Willie, oh lets not forget that pillar of the public, simple Simon, all we are short of is your Jew- boy friend." Herman was just about to start on someone else when Brendan interrupted.

"Would you be der feller dat has half der town held tu ransom, would dat be you now boyo," said Brendan standing up and looking quite menacing.

"This isn't your business Paddy, I've not forgot the last time we met, you'll get yours when I'm ready," said Herman, not too keen to start mixing it with the big Irishman. "What's the problem," asked Brendan. "Frightened tu get your pretty new suit dirty." Then Willie, who had slipped under the table piped up.

"Call that a suit, he slurred--- av seen better dressed *wounds* than that." The pub was in uproar, even Simon had a smile. "And that bloody coat---hic---yer wearing looks more like a whippets smoking jacket---hic---with all that bloody velvet round the collar." If anything in the world got up Herman's nose it was being made fun of. He smashed his large fist down onto the table under which Willie was lying. Crash went the glasses onto the floor.

Brendan expecting the worst, stood between Herman and the cowering Willie, the minders waiting for the word from their boss to be let loose.

"You've not heard the last of this Watson and the rest of you scum." Brendan taking offence at being called scum was getting ready for an all out assault when Maxine whispered in his ear that one of the heavies had a knife behind his back. Even Brendan knew that this wasn't the time.

Herman and his men backed out of the room shouting a threat to all, that this was just the beginning, with a special warning to me that he would make me suffer in more ways than one.

Jill grabbed my arm, a look of fear etched on her face, I tried to reassure her that this was just an empty threat, Herman was just trying to show that he was still the kingpin in the area--- but deep down my gut feeling was telling me different. Brendan still keen on having a go at the retreating thugs had a final dig at Herman. "Be Jesus yer big lump of shit let me be telling *you,*" he shouted."If ders any ting happens to Tom or his family, or anyone else dat yer care tu try and frighten, you'll be having a problem worse dan yer worst nightmare, so keep dat in yer mind Mister."

The thugs left the pub, slamming the door behind them breaking the glass panels into little pieces. The atmosphere in the room was very tense to say the least. We decided to call it a night so we bid our farewells to all and headed towards the broken door where Simon was busy trying to clean up the mess. His sheepish look told me that there was more to this visit from Herman than he was letting on, but this wasn't the place or the time to question him. That would have to wait.

Jill and I had just got a few yards from the pub when we heard hurried footsteps behind us. I bent down to pick up a handy half brick and turned swiftly only to see Brendan and Maxine.

"Ah tort Max and me would be keeping yer company so ah did, tis a lovely night fer walking so it is," said an out of breath Brendan.

"But you and Max live in the opposite direction." "Be Jesus yer right Tom, it must be great having a local knowledge like yerself and here's meself and Max tinking we were going in der right direction---if yer know what ah mean Tom."

"Not really Brendan, but we won't go into that now."

It was plain to see Brendan was just looking out for our safety and to be quite honest I felt a lot more at ease with him along for company. It wasn't Herman's way to follow up a confrontation so quickly, he normally left it for at least a week or more just in case the police had been tipped off and the wrong coppers turned up, (the honest ones) not his paid cronies.

After being accompanied by Brendan and Maxine right to the door they declined an invitation for a cup of tea, it might have been another story had it been whisky. They both made their excuses and waltzed off holding hands like a couple of love struck teenagers on a first date.

Two weeks had gone by and it was like living in a cage. One of us at the kennels while the other one took the kids to school. The kids couldn't understand why they were being chaperoned everywhere, but grudgingly went along with it. We decided it was time for a few home truths. Jill and I sat them down and told them the reason why we had to keep a close eye on them.

Colin, the oldest sat there on the settee looking at the pair of us. "Dad, we aren't stupid, you can't wrap us up in cotton wool forever, we knew there something wrong by the way you and Mam have been acting, now that you've told us the problem you can't let a thug like Herman rule our lives, can yer?"

The boy was right; I looked at Jill, tears rolling down her cheeks, her face full of pride for our oldest son.

"Tom Watson," she said with a determined tone in her voice. "From tomorrow we live our lives like we should, I'm dammed if I'm going ter let a scumbag like Herman keep me and my family in fear." "Why can't we start from tunight dad, instead of in the morning, then we can go out and play with Billy Wilson's new football," said Paul our youngest.

"Why the hell not," I replied. Colin was right we had to get on with things and take each day as it came.

CHAPTER FOURTEEN

Four weeks had gone by without incident; as usual things weren't looking to good in the financial department. Lucky had bruised his toe running around in the paddock and wasn't quite ready for a race. Our only chance was a little black bitch that had just finished her season break. (Lady) was her pet name. She was a bitch that came to hand very quickly after being in season.

The problem was trying to find a race where she would be treated fairly, and that was something that wouldn't be easy.

The only track Lady hadn't raced at was Ships End, Barry Martin's track, Mr arrogance himself. I hadn't forgotten that I owed Mr smart arse one and I knew the right man to help me get a little revenge, plus a few quid into the bargain, Tommy the cap.

Tommy also had a black bitch, not as fast as Lady but that I hoped, would work in our favour. The plan was to steady Lady down for her trial, give her a few gallops, or take her to the local pond and let her swim until she got tired, just enough to take the edge away from her best form.

Tommy the cap was contacted and was only to pleased to go along with the plan. He had a score to settle with the handicapper, plus as usual he was skint. Tommy was to take Lady for a trial and let the handicapper and the punters think it was his bitch. We weren't doing anything illegal in a sense! Tommy was taking in a black bitch, if the handicapper and the

119

public thought the bitch was Tommy's, that was their prerogative, then so be it.

On the day of the trial we met Tommy and handed over Lady with instructions to meet us after the trial at an old industrial estate about three miles from the track.

We'd only been there about half an hour when Tommy pulled up with his mate big Alan. I feared the worst until I saw those pearly white teeth of Tommy's shining through that scraggy beard of his, with a grin from ear to ear as we put lady into the van.

"Any problems, Tommy," I asked.

"Only a few dogs there Tom, we were in the first trial, the bitch led out but started tu fade coming off the last bend, av entered her for next week, ah think the handicapper seemed desperate for dogs, so ah thought this was the right time tu get her on the card."

"Yer did right Tommy, next week will be just the job." Alan seemed a little impatient as he sat there revving up the engine.

"Tommy," shouted Allan,

"That bloody hoss is running in the two-thirty if we miss it and it wins am gona kill yer."

"That's nowt new, me getting threats off Alan," said Tommy walking towards Alan's car the revs getting louder by the second. "Oh by the way Tom, one or two of the punters and the handicapper thought that she was my old bitch, mind you, looking at them there's not a lot of difference is there!"

Little did Tommy know there was a major difference in that Lady had a big white blaze from her chin to the middle of her forelegs, Tommy's bitch had just a little white between her front legs. We thought it best for Tommy not to know that

120

we had blacked out the white on Lady's chest, at least for the time being.

Next problem was trying to find a little betting money before next weeks race and the chances were slim, very slim indeed. Jimmy the beard was in the same boat as me, he'd had an accident working down the pit and like me had to depend on making a few quid with the dogs to survive. In my situation there was only one thing to do! Pay a visit to the Pawnshop.

I had pawned so much jewellery in that shop that in the end I didn't know if it was his or mine. It wasn't as if it was worth a fortune, a sovereign ring and a couple of men's gold bracelets worth about £70. Jill knew nothing of these things that I'd bought in my younger days and had kept them for a rainy day. It was more like a bloody rain forest the amount of times this stuff had to go down to that shop. But what had to be done had to be done.

I retrieved the rings etc. from their safe keeping and headed off to Mr Duggan's shop. He was sprightly old soul with a weather-beaten face, big bushy eyebrows and just as many hairs coming from his ears.

"Now Tom me lad, what can ah be doing yer for."
"You're not wrong there Mr Duggan, you'll be trying tu do us for a few quid more than likely."

"Tom yer know me better dan dat so yer do, have ah not always given yer der best price possible?"

"Yer have Mr Duggan am only joking with yer." I had to be very careful what I said; I needed the best price possible.

"What have yer got Tom, the usual." "That's right Mr Duggan," I replied with a grin, hoping that he may pay a little extra, no such luck as he counted out £70 exactly.

"Yer wouldn't be wanting dis money for a wee bet Tom, would yer," he asked as he twiddled his long bushy eyebrows.

"Because if dat were der case--- mind you I'm not asking so I'm not, but if it were der case ah might be stretching dat pawn money tu £80, plus a tenner for meself and ah don't want tu know where or when der dog is running---now ah can't be saying fairer dan dat."

The old man looked at me with that old weather-beaten face and held out his hand. I shook hands with him just as an old lady burst through the door holding a mountain of clothing way above her head, she stopped only when her feet clattered into the counter. I bid my farewells with clothing falling all around me and said I'd hope to see him soon, trying to avoid standing on the old lady's garments scattered on the floor.

Billy had been lucky on the horses backing a 20/1 straight win, but that was Billy, all or nothing, no each way, straight win. JW worked for a firm picking up meat from the slaughter-houses, suffice to say we were very rarely without a nice piece of meat, liver, sausage and pork. I half expected to walk into the pantry one day and find a cow hanging up, but that was JW nothing was safe in the meat line when he was on his rounds, fiddle should have been his middle name.

Perhaps our luck was about to change, God knows we needed it, at least we all had a few quid for a bet on Lady, all we wanted now was the right mark in the right race.

The news was good; Tommy had been in touch and had told me that Lady was in a level break and that he'd called her (Black Swan). He had also given the names of the dogs Lady was running against. After studying the form and making some discreet enquiries, we had to make our minds up.

The five dogs in the race were all known to us, with the exception of one, we could beat four of them, should we take the chance and gamble that we could beat the unknown dog? Or do we wait for another day. These were difficult times and serious decisions had to be made. Jill and I needed the money for one or two bills that had to be paid, the little terraced house we lived in was ours bought and paid for with money Jill and I had saved over the years. A ramshackle of a place when we bought it for little money, but with a lot of hard work we were getting there and Jill loved her little house.

We also needed the money for a gamble on Lucky now that his toe had healed, hopefully Lady would provide enough for both. The decision had been taken to take our chance, the odds had been narrowed down to just that one dog to beat.

Tommy the cap had come to collect our money and the dog, with instructions to use his own men for the betting. I was to go into the track myself, not to draw to much attention and decide if we were to take on the unknown dog in the race.

As I entered the paddock, the dog in question stood out a mile, a big strong looking brindle dog that looked a real picture. I had arranged with Tommy that if the gamble was not to go ahead, I would signal him by blowing my nose, he was then to place the elastic band around Lady's foot. This did no harm to the dog, but made it very uncomfortable to run.

I was just about to leave the paddock area when someone tapped me on the shoulder from behind, I turned to see a very good friend of mine called Twitcher Murphy, a nickname no one dare call him to his face. Harry was his real name; he got the twitch from the continuous beatings he'd received from his drunkard of a father, who also gave Harry's mother beatings regularly. I'd known Harry since childhood when he'd call round to my gran's house for a bite to eat, or to have his wounds attended to.

Things started to change when Harry got older and stronger. Sick of the beatings to himself and his mother, he lay in wait one night knowing his father would be coming in drunk and that he or his mother would be on the receiving end of yet another beating. I remember clearly how Harry had confided to me what he was going to do and what he wanted me to do. I had to call at his house with a message for his mother that I'd bumped into a relative who wanted to see her. I played my part then ran as fast as I could to my house and waited for the event to happen.

I didn't have long to wait before the street was alive with police sirens. I sat at the top of the stairs my knees shaking with fear.

It wasn't long before there was a knock at the door. "Mary, Mary," cried the voice in sheer panic.

"Young Harry Murphy's shot his mother and father, blood everywhere Mary, everywhere," shouted the neighbour. My heart was pounding, no, no, I kept saying to myself, this had to be a mistake.

Harry loved his mother more than anything in the world and wouldn't hurt a hair on her head. I remember coming down the stairs two at a time and running out into the street. I ran to Harry's house, an ambulance was parked outside the door. People were scurrying from door to door with all sorts of rumours. Harry's door opened as two ambulance men carried someone out on a stretcher. I held my breath, dreading that it might be Harry's mother, or even Harry himself. If things had gone wrong, I would never be able to forgive myself. When I learned that it was the old man, a sigh of relief ran through my body. The local bobby, Mr Jobsen soon filled in the locals as to what had happened. Harry had waited in the dark of the room until he was sure it was his father coming through that door, then gave him both barrels hitting his leg and one of his arms.

Harry did time for that and came out of prison a very hard and bitter man. His poor mother had died while he was inside, his father had left the village fearing what his son would do on his release.

If Herman had a fear of anyone, it was Twitcher Murphy. Harry had been missing for some length of time and I didn't like to ask the reason why.

He shook my hand with a passion and he really looked as if he was pleased to see me. "How's the wife and kids Tom, me mother kept me in touch with what was happening when I was inside, she told me about you getting married and having a family, there's not much ah don't know about what's being going on Tom and ah still owe yer big time for that favour yer did for me."

"Forget about the past Harry, there were good times and bad, but we still had a laugh or two." We strode towards the bookies; two rough looking minders matching strides as I hastily increased my pace. "Fancy anything in this race Tom," Harry asked. Shit I thought to myself, do I tell him, or what!

"Av er heard a whisper for the two dog Black Swan Harry, *but* that's only if there's any money for it." The words hadn't left my mouth when the rush came for the unknown dog Morrissey, running from trap six. Tommy's team held back on my instructions to wait until the last seconds.Harry's minders were stood either side of me, the crowd milled around trying to bet this apparent good thing, I couldn't move, I could hardly breath.

There was no chance of me trying to signal Tommy, my arms were jammed by my side by Harry's minders, I was unable to move a muscle, panic was starting to set in.

The six dog Morrissey was backed off the board, not a price to be had anywhere. Lady's price had drifted out to 5-1, it was too late to do anything. Tommy's lads had backed the bitch at 5-1. Harry looked at me his face twitching like mad. "Is it worth a bet Tom, this Black Swan, the price on the favourite isn't worth a bet." I thought to myself, sink or swim, my money's on and the bitch is doing her best, if she runs like she can, we have a chance.

"Have a few quid on Black Swan, Harry, at least its value." Harry whispered into one of the minders ears and out came a bundle of notes that would have choked a hippo, he peeled off a bundle of £5 notes and went along the line of the ten bookies with £200 a book. I closed my eyes at the thought of the consequences if the bitch were to be beaten.

The Harry Murphy I knew could lose his rag at the least disappointment, especially a bet. I'd seen him beat up kids when we were at school if they'd beaten him at pitch and toss and that was for pennies. God knows what he'd do if he lost a few hundred pounds! Too late to worry, the traps had gone up and the dogs were racing.

Lady, (Black Swan) and Morrissey were neck and neck around the first bend, this was going to be touch and go with Morrissey moving slightly off the bends and Lady sticking to the rails like shit to a blanket. They were coming to the last bend Morrissey moved out wide, a possible sign that the dog may not have been around the track before. That gave Lady the advantage on the run in, please don't let this be a photo finish I muttered to myself, even if we win, the decision would go against us. I had a gut feeling that Morrissey had been placed in the race to win by the handicapper. The dogs flashed past the winning post, I'd no idea who had won.

Harry, who was just about the same height as me, was also in the dark. The punters were in no doubt that Black Swan had won by at least a neck and maybe more, but with this handicapper, anything could happen, if he could wangle it for Morrissey to win, he would do so.

Harry was becoming very impatient. The handicapper was taking his time with the result and was no doubt trying to fix the outcome of the race if Black Swan had won. Harry and his minders walked towards the judge's box.

"What's the delay," demanded Harry as he burst open the door.

"You'll get the result when I'm ready tu give it tu yer," said the judge with his back towards the door looking at the photo and trying to work out how to reverse the placing's. Harry asked once more. "Why the delay." The handicapper half turned ready to give a tirade of abuse to the voice demanding the result. "Av just told yer," were the words he managed to release from his mouth---- before he realised who was standing in the doorway. "Bad---er print—that's it, bad print Harry," said the snivelling handicapper as his hands shook with fear.

"This old er equipment, just about had it." "The result," demanded Harry. "Er what did yer back Harry," asked the handicapper not wanting to upset the impatient Harry by giving off the wrong result. "The two dog, Black Swan," he replied. "You've backed a winner, a good neck Harry, a good neck," the handicapper repeated. "Don't even know why ah wanted a photo, al give if off on the mike now."

The result was given off to the waiting crowd, much to the joy of Tommy and his team, also Billy, Jimmy and JW who were just entering the track. Harry collected his winnings and shoved £100 into my hand. "Before yer say anything Tom, *don't,* no doubt we'll bump into each other from time tu time, things tu do and places tu go, I'm always there if you need anything Tom, take care."

With that Harry walked out through the gates not a care in the world, his minders by his side. I'd heard rumours about Harry and the business he was in, none of it I'm glad to say included drugs, or hurting innocent people. I would always have a soft spot for Harry, remembering the beatings and the hard life he'd had, also remembering what he could do to anyone that crossed him. I'd seen what he'd done to his father after he'd recovered and it wasn't a pretty sight.

Harry had made sure that night of the shooting, that his father wouldn't be in a fit state to continue the beating of his mother. Only he knows if he meant to cripple, or kill him, either way his old man was barely capable of making himself a cup of tea, never mind beating someone.

I left the track with Billy and company to meet up with Tommy at the arranged meeting place. He stood outside the car with a smile stretching from ear to ear, his mates hadn't arrived with the winnings and Tommy wasn't sure if we had bet Lady or not. So I decided to have a bit of fun with him.

"What happened with the elastic band Tommy, Lady's won and we haven't had a bean on her, what the hell were yer playing at?" The expression on his face went from a large grin to a gob smacked open mouth. "Tom ah swear tu God ah never saw any signal, in fact ah never even saw *YOU.*"

I was finding it hard to keep a straight face, especially with JW and everyone in the background nearly doubled up in kinks.

In the end we had to give in, much to the relief of Tommy who by this time had several kicks at his mates old car. "You stinking rotten lot, you've got me in a right state thinking it's me tu blame for the job going wrong and not putting the elastic band on the dogs foot." I was doubled up with laughter and couldn't say a word. "While we are on about the dog Mr Watson, am like a bloody black and white minstrel, me hands are covered in black stuff, me grey flannels are black, our lass will go mad."

He was just about to let blast with another volley when his team turned up. The expression on Tommy's face soon turned to delight when he heard the price the lads had got for Lady. "Five tu one," Alan shouted. "Five tu one, it's another wind up, yer taking the Mickey, howay lads stop messing about am missing out on a pint or two, plus am playing cards with Shifty Morris." "Shifty Morris," I said, "Yer must be joking yer couldn't beat Shifty with *five aces,* do me a favour Tommy, have your couple of pints and save your money till next week."

"Why next week," asked Tommy. "Because av a feeling that the little bitch just might win again."

I had a hunch that if Lady were entered into a race at Barry Martins track again she would not be without a chance, not after the visit from Harry Twitcher Murphy. I was hoping that the handicapper might think there was some connection and treat the bitch fairly at least.

129

After some careful thinking Tommy the cap took his share of the winnings and headed home--- via the Fat Goose pub for a couple of quick ones.

Billy and the rest of the lads divided their winnings with smiling faces, all in all the night had turned out better than we had expected. My take was £460 plus my £90 stake and the £100 drink Twitcher had given me, not forgetting Mr Duggan's £10 stake and his winnings to be deducted from mine.

Next stop Mrs Moffit's fish shop."Usual Mrs Moffit," I said. "Nu nu nu no Jill tu tunight Tttoom." Not tunight Mrs Moffit—lads night out." "Ttttom Watttson you've bbeen coming here ttoo long tu bbe tteling mme pporkies, Jjjill and yyou are like bbbony and cclyde nnever ffar aappart, bbuut aall ssay nu more, a hhope yyer bbbacked a wwinner." "Ah did Mrs Moffit, but that's between me you and the man upstairs."

She quickly wrapped up the fish and chips, quicker than she was able to put her sentences together, poor old girl. I bid her goodnight then drove straight home to Jill and the kids. The kids were still up waiting in expectation of Lady winning and getting stuck into their suppers, the steam from the hot fish and chips wrapped in yesterdays newspaper a big hint as to how the race had turned out. Paul our youngest was already making his way to the table armed with a knife fork and four slices of bread.

The broad smile on Jill's face showed the relief of knowing she'd be able to pay the bills that were outstanding, gas and electricity. Both Jill and myself hated the pressure of debt, when we couldn't afford to buy something; we would save until we could. I'd been brought up in an environment

130

where debt was part of the norm. Where people could be evicted and their belongings thrown onto the street, all because the man of the house had lost his job through ill-health and fallen behind with the rent, or his face didn't fit with one of his so called superiors at the pit.

I'd sworn from those days that there would be none of that for me, my old Grandfather who I'd been brought up by, always told me---if you don't smoke or drink, you may never be rich, but you'll always have a better chance of keeping a roof over your head, he was right, I wasn't rich, but the roof over my head was our own.

Waking up the next day and seeing the sun shining through the window seemed to breath new life into the whole family. Jill with a smile that could fill a room, the kids full of excitement of what they might be getting in the way of new clothes, not that they were demanding in any way, they were just the opposite, always happy for what came their way.

I'd given Jill £300, this left me with £280 of which £80 was to go back to Mr Duggan to redeem the contents from the pawn ticket I was holding, along with his winnings of £60. While Jill was busy paying off the bills and doing some shopping for the kids, I was up at the kennels seeing to the dogs before my business at the Pawnshop.

Lucky's bruised toe had healed well, another week with a little more work and he'd be ready for a race. That was something I was really looking forward to. I left the kennels and made my way down to the Pawnshop.

I pushed open the door to the deafening clang of the bell's that hung from the ceiling above the door. There was no way anyone was going to sneak into Mr Duggan's shop without him hearing.

I'm sure he brought those bells with him from Ireland when he first arrived here, they made enough noise to summon all the Catholics in the neighbourhood to mass. "Is der someone der," came a voice from the top of the stairs.

"Only a near deaf Protestant Mr Duggan," I replied, as a head popped round from the top of the open banister. "Be Jesus is dat you Tom, have ah converted yer tu be a good Catholic boy wit me bells, if yer not going tu convert yer can be going out and coming in again so yer can."

I took out the roll of notes and flashed them as I opened the door just a little, so as not to disturb those deafening bells as I pretended to leave.

"Be Jesus can yer not be taking a joke young Tom, flashing money like dat can turn a man intu any religion he likes so it can--- er what religion would yer be sir," he asked. "The kind that likes tu pay his debts on time Mr Duggan--- is there any other kind." "Be Jesus ah wish all dem lost souls out der dat hasn't paid tu redeem der goods would be having der same religion as yerself so I do." Mr Duggan took the stairs two at a time and he nearly broke his neck as he stumbled on the last two.

"Would I be correct in tinking der gamble paid off Tom," said Mr Duggan his big bushy eyebrows and hairy ear's looking more prominent than ever. "That would be correct sir, £10 on at five to one gives you £60 and then there's the little matter of the £80 plus for the loan."

"We'll not be bothering with der plus young Tom so we won't, I'll be quite happy wit der winnings and a half chance of a conversion of yer religion, ah tink maybe ders a slim chance dat we'll be getting yer some day so we will." I counted out the money on Mr Duggan's counter, shook his

132

hand picked up my ring and bracelets and bid him good morning.

I'd just left the shop when I bumped into Jill. "What you doing down this end of the town," she asked. "Me er---er lucking for you sweetheart," I replied.

I was desperately looking for a satisfactory excuse to keep Jill from asking any more questions, God knows what I would have said if I'd been caught coming out of the Pawnshop.

As we walked back up to the town, Jill was telling me what she'd bought for the kids and that she'd paid off the bills. We decided to call into old Jacob's shop and found him busy at work. "Plenty work on Jacob," I asked, as he lifted his head from his little treadle sewing machine and peered over his wire-rimmed glasses, his big black hat covering his long grey hair.

"Tom, Jill how nice to see you already, how are those boys of yours," he asked as he rubbed his hard working hands together. "Fine just fine," I replied.

"You seem tu have plenty of work on, maybe this is not the best time tu call." "For my two best friends anytime is a good time, sit down sit, sit, we have what you call tea break."

We tried to tell the old man that we had to get back--but he was having none of it as he busied himself making the tea and breaking out his favourite biscuit's, Rich Tea. "Eat Tom eat, if you are going to dip, you have to be quick, the rascals they fall back into your tea before you can catch them." The words hardly left his mouth before he was juggling to try and save the inevitable. "You see what I mean Tom, maybe next time I get ginger snaps."

After a good chat Jill and I drank our tea and bid the old man goodbye. There was no mention of that scumbag Herman and it was obvious the old man was happy at his work, so I decided to let sleeping dogs lie. We were just leaving the shop when the old man caught my arm and whispered, "Tom my boy, if ever you need my help, in any way, no matter what, you can count on me my boy."

"That's nice tu hear Jacob and I won't forget." I shook the old mans half gloved hand and went on our way.

Halfway up the old cobbled street passing Tony the Greeks café, I caught sight of Tommy the cap having a pot of tea with his drinking mates.

Jill and I were standing looking through the window at four of the saddest faces in the village. Tony the proprietor saw us at the window and beckoned us in.

"Tom, what can you do to make theses---theses friends of yours smile, It's a bad for business, people they are thinking it's not good food." Tony was right, they all had faces liked smacked arses. When Tommy and his friends raised their heads, they looked even worse. "Don't tell me you've been on the drink all night, look at the state of yer---- *Av seen more smiles in a piles clinic*," a chuckle came from Tony, an intense look from Tommy as if to say, that's not the worst of it.

Then the penny dropped, "Tommy don't tell me you've been playing cards with Swifty Morris, ah wouldn't play *pitch and toss* with Swifty if a had a two headed coin, the mans lethal, come on where's your brain."

I asked Tommy how much he'd lost. Tommy gave me a guilty look and a shrug of his shoulders. "Lost the lot Tom, am sure he was cheating." "Bet yer bloody life he was cheating, the last time somebody played pitch and toss with Swifty they couldn't find the coins at the end of the match."

134

"Anyway Tommy, the damage is done, get yerself pulled round for next week, with a bit of luck the bitch might have half a squeak." I left the café as Tony shouted. "You make him worse Tom, what my customers say now!" "Tell them not tu play cards with Swifty Morris,." I replied. "Very funny Tom, but I no laugh."

The week went quickly by, it's amazing how a few quid in your pocket makes things a lot easier. Lucky was sound again and ready for a run.

Billy called with a race card for the meeting at Ships End track. Lady was in a level break and had a more than an even chance.

There was also an open race that hadn't been filled. If our suspicions were right, the track was short of dogs so the handicapper had to make the card up with an open race.

This might be an opportunity to kill two birds with one stone; we could also run Lucky in the open. I was just finalising the last few details with Billy when Jill came out with a bombshell.

"Ah hope you haven't forgotten we are out for a meal with Jimmy and Margaret tunight, it's been booked for ages, yer can't let them down, it's their wedding anniversary."

Shit I thought tu myself, tunight of all nights. Jimmy and Margaret were good friends, Jill was right we had to be there, the only thing to do was to get Tommy the cap to pick up Lady and the betting money from Billy at the kennels. Billy could then see to Lucky for the open race. My bet was £200 on Lady, this was her second run after being in season and I expected her to be a whole lot better. The winnings, if any were to go on Lucky, all but £50. I was desperate to see Lucky race, but what had to be, had to be. Jimmy had been in

135

touch just to confirm that everything was going to plan and that he was going to ring Margaret at the clothing factory where she worked to see if there was any chance of an early finish. I could read into Jimmy's thinking, an early meal could mean we had a slim chance of seeing at least one of the dogs run.

Late afternoon, Jimmy phoned Margaret's work. "Excuse me, would it be possible to speak to Mrs Margaret Bell please."

"Who's speaking," came the posh voice on the other end of the phone." "It's Mr Bell," Jimmy replied.

"We don't normally take calls unless they are urgent." Jimmy paused for a second or two, then replied.

"Tell my wife that the *Black Swan is on the village pond.*" There was silence for a second or two, then the voice said. *"I'll call her straight away."* Jimmy was all on to keep from laughing his head off. Margaret came to the phone at sixes and sevens trying to understand the problem and gave Jimmy a right mouth full. "What bloody Black Swan, what the hell are yer talking about?" "Just keep quiet and look concerned when you put down the phone, you've got a short shift, see you soon bye." Before Margaret could reply, Jimmy had replaced the phone.

Later that night we met at a quiet little pub called the *Fountain Inn,* Margaret had forgiven Jimmy by then and we were all enjoying our meal, When I suddenly jumped to my feet nearly knocking over my plate and startling the other diners. I'd forgotten to darken down the white on Lady's chest. I quickly glanced at my watch, if the race was on time Lady would have either been withdrawn, with Tommy in a heap of trouble, or she'd have run and hopefully won. From

136

that moment on, the evening was ruined. Both Jill and Margaret could see the problem and very politely suggested we leave. Jimmy and his wife had been given a lift by a neighbour to the pub, the only thing I could do now was to take them home in the van, then head straight for the track.

With a bit of luck we might just be in time to catch Lucky's race. Everything was going smoothly when the inevitable happened, a puncture, that's all we needed. By the time I'd changed the wheel and reached the track the last race had been run. When I eventually found Tommy who had taken Lady back to her kennel and returned to the track for the remainder of the meeting.

The smile on his face said it all. "How did things go Tommy," I asked with a bit of trepidation.

"Not to bad Tom, considering," came his reply. "Oh, Oh," I thought something has gone amiss. "What's the problem Tommy?" "Not what you'd call a problem Tom, just a bit short in the price, 2-1 ah think we were spoiled with the 5-1 we had last week." A feeling of relief filtered through my body, with no mention of Lady's white chest.

Jill and I stood behind the van while Tommy counted out the winnings for the lads and me. We were just about to open the van doors to leave, when Tommy shouted, "The Black dog ran a good race Tom." Great I thought to myself as I rubbed my hands together, double off, then the bombshell dropped. "Beaten a couple of lengths in a very fast time by a cracking good dog." My heart sank; Jill and I jumped into the van and sped off home. Doris, Jill's mother who had been babysitting was surprised to see us.

"Yer early our Jill, ah thought yer might have gone back tu Jimmy's and Margaret's." "Not tu-night mam, early start in the morning," said Jill, trying not to look too despondent. "Maybe just as well for me love getting home early, your dads on first shift he'll just be going tu bed." There was no sign of Billy as I looked out of the door and ushered Doris quickly into the van. "Just be a few minutes Jill while I run your mother over, er---I mean home sweetheart, home, just kidding."

I grinned as Doris gave me one of her scowling looks that she'd give Jill's dad when things weren't going her way. I'd only gone a few hundred yards down the road when I caught sight of Billy's little blue car coming in the other direction, I hit the accelerator and sped off to Doris's house, she'd hardly got her foot out of the van before I was off. Leaving her shouting in the background as she gained her balance and pulled herself together.

"You bloody lunatic Tom Watson--- you keep them kids out of that van till yer learn tu bloody drive." Doris was not pleased to say the least as she stood there shaking her fist, then covering her mouth with her hand realising that Tommy, her husband may have already gone to bed.

Billy was waiting outside when I arrived back home. "Before yer ask Tom, it was the same black dog that beat Lucky the last time, *Just Black*, No excuse Tom, no shame either, we were beaten fair and square, it's gunner take one hell of a dog tu beat that feller, the only thing tu hope for is that we don't bump intu him to often." Billy was right we were going to have pick our races with great care. "It was him Tom, *Just Black* for definite, by the time ad got close enough tu check the moles on his face just to make sure, it was to late tu call off the bet." "Not tu worry Bill, we've been in worse situations than this and came out on top, our time will come,

138

time and patience Bill, time and patience." I was trying to make light of the defeat, as if I didn't care, but if the truth was known I felt sick to my stomach.

CHAPTER FIFTEEN

Herman was in the area increasing his activities, rumours of beatings for those who were late with their protection money and humiliation for the girls working in his brothels for not earning enough.

This was the last thing in the world I wanted to hear. Jill had gone to her mother's and I hoped and prayed that the rumours had not reached the isolated row of terraced houses where Jill's parents lived. There were no shops or people of means to be threatened by Herman's bully-boy tactics.

I was quietly reading the paper when there was a knock on the door, it startled me at first thinking it might be Herman, or one of his cronies, but they wouldn't knock, they'd burst in or knock the door off it's hinges. I picked up the poker from the fireside and gingerly started to open the door, I was surprised to see my old mate Simon Long from the Pig and Whistle.

"How's things Simon?" I asked the gaunt looking figure standing in my doorway. "Is er-- Jill in Tom," asked Simon looking round the room. "No Simon she's at her mothers, why?" "There's something I want to discuss Tom---and I'd prefer Jill wasn't here," he said in his quiet but clear-cut voice, no slang words, Simon was a very polite young man.

Once he'd started to talk there was no stopping him, it was as if he'd had this problem bottled up inside him for years and couldn't stop it from just pouring out.

His story was amazing and to be honest I half expected some of the things he was telling me--- but not the full extent of this horrific tale, what Simon must have been going through, beggars belief.

Having talked for an hour or so non-stop, Simon looked a relieved and different person. He may have got some things off his chest by talking to me, but his problem was still there. How to deal with it was another matter, it was a near impossibility--- short of shooting someone!

Simon stood up to leave, a little colour coming back to his ashen face. Unfortunately all Simon had done was burden me with his problem.

There had to be a way out of this for everyone's sake, but it wasn't going to be easy.

Simon had just left when Jill arrived back from her mother's. "Was that Simon Long leaving, Tom, unusual Simon calling at this time of day with a pub tu run?" she said, a curious look on her face. "Been er, er looking for a chap that er, owes him money love, asking if ah new where he lived, or if I'd heard of him." "What's his name?" asked Jill as she took the contents from her shopping bag and placed them in the cupboard.

"You wouldn't know him, er --- stranger round here pet, ran a slate up at Simons then must have done a moonlight." "So what's his name?" repeated Jill being most persistent.

Shit I thought to myself, she's not going to give in until I give her a name. "Charley Blenkinsopp," I replied, I had to say something and it was the first name that came into my head, where the hell I'd thought of that name I'll never know.

"Charley Blenkinsop," Jill snapped. "Am not surprised he's done a moonlight with a name like that--- God bless me mam and dad with a name like Fisher." The heat was off, Jill satisfied that Simon's visit was to collect a debt from our

141

imaginary friend Mr Blenkinsopp, a slight problem solved, a major problem still loomed.

My main concern was to keep a close eye on Jill and the kids, since she had arrived back from her mother's there'd been no mention of Herman.

One week on and still no word of Herman, I'd started to relax a little, licked my wounds and had Lucky back on the card in an open race at Mr Ryan's Downhill track. We had decided to take the kids for a night out, I'd been a bit mean with them restricting their movements knowing Herman had been seen in the village. Jill was overjoyed the kids were going to the track and couldn't understand why the restrictions were on in the first place.

It was nice to be out as a family, we bumped into Brendan and Maxine, then Stringvest Willie with his intended Anytime Annie. It was just like old times; Billy and the lads were bringing Lucky to the track to avoid the dog being in the van with the now excited kids larking about.

Dark clouds had started to form and it wasn't long before the heavens opened, we all scattered to the shelter of the clubhouse, Willie being last of course, just in case he had to buy a round of drinks.

"Will de owners of der dogs in der *respective* races---be Jesus isn't dat a grand word so it is, *respective,* er-- please take dem straight tu der traps as it's a filty night so it is." Lucky was in the sixth race, the dogs in race four were heading straight to the traps, there was no parading of the dogs as the rain lashed down, with some poor dogs without walking out coats to protect them. Mr Ryan was doing his best to run the races off as quickly as possible. In no time the announcement came for our race, the sixth.

"All dogs run in de open race, please take dem dogs straight tu der starting traps, now hurry along please, der trap draw is as follows, trap one is Sampson, two is TJ (Lucky), tree is Jenny, four is Topper, five is Jack in the box, and trap six is Skint again." The rain was coming down in buckets; the track was like a bog.

The chance of studying the opposition before the race was impossible as they were directed straight to the traps, we couldn't even see the traps.

I'd decided along with the lads this wasn't the night to be gambling, the track heavy, the rain lashing into the dogs faces, this wasn't for me. But it was for some brave gamblers as the bookmakers shouted the odds of 1-2 on the four dog Topper. We were drawn trap two. I felt sorry for poor Billy, in the thick of it on the track, while the rest of the lads stood round the big open fire.

"How anyone can back a dog at 1-2 in these conditions must be crazy." "Yer right there Tom, they have tu be out of their tiny minds," said Jimmy the beard.

"Ad still back it at 1-2," said Willie the vest. Jimmy and myself looked at each other and shook our heads. "Exactly Willie, like ah said, out of their tiny minds."

The announcement came to place the dogs into the traps. Everyone vying for a vantage point from inside the building, standing on tables and chairs, it was nearly impossible to see through the steamed up windows, there were more window cleaners in that clubhouse waving their hands than there was in all of Co Durham.

"The hares running," crackled the loudspeaker as sparks bounced off the wall of the clubhouse from the metal container housing the equipment.

I'd managed to find a half decent viewing point, but the visibility was so bad that we were going to have to rely on the judge Mr Ryan for the result. At least he had a better view than the punters, no steamed up windows to contend with and no one to block his view of the race.

The first two dogs that came into sight from the last bend was either *four and two, or two and four*. Both black dogs and both racing jackets covered in mud, from my view it was impossible to distinguish which number was which! Then came the announcement, first number------- the interference from the old speaker was like someone eating a dozen packets of crisps right next to your ear. Mr Ryan had another attempt, "First number ----Four Topper, second number Two TJ. Der time be Jesus is a terrible time so it is 28-60 and der winner won by tree lents." The time was bad, but my main concern was that Lucky had come out of the race unscathed.

The time of the race and the distance was of little consequence, even getting beat was immaterial, as we hadn't had a bet. I gathered up Jill and the kids and braved the elements. The rain was still lashing down not letting up at all. We had just got to the car park when we could faintly hear Mr Ryan on the old speaker giving out that the rest of the meeting was to be abandoned.

Billy had the good sense to take Lucky straight home for a good dry off and rub down with a special liniment, the recipe of this had been handed down over the years.

We hurried into the house to the warmth of a roaring open fire that Billy had stacked up when he got back from the track. "Right kids," shouted Jill.

"Up them stairs, wet clothes off, jamas on then back down for something hot before bed." Lucky looked quite happy

144

stretched out on the clippie mat in front of the fire, not a care in the world. "Av had a good luk at im Tom, seems ok tu me," said Billy shaking his head.

"Problem Bill," I asked. "Not to sure Tom, it's---it's just something on me mind, ah couldn't swear tur it Tom, but that winner tunight bore a strong resemblance tu our old friend Just Black."

A cold shiver ran down my spine and I don't think it was anything to do with the weather.

"That's three times we've met that dog, if it is him---and three times he's licked us." "How sure can yer be Billy," I asked hoping that deep down Billy could be totally wrong.

"Luk at the facts Tom, bearing in mind that ah had a better view of the race than you, the way that the winner started from the traps, his style of running, the amount of money that's been shovelled on each time he's won, most of all the distance he's beaten Lucky in every race, about three lengths each time." Billy was right, the coincidences all added up.

We had to accept that but for a miracle, Lucky was never going to beat *Just Black.*Billy left the house to face the rain that was still lashing down, Jill and I had decided to leave Lucky in the house for the night, he'd eaten his dinner and it seemed a shame to disturb him laying there flat out in front of the fire, I'll pop him back up to the kennels first thing in the morning.

A week had passed since that dreadful storm and things were looking a bit grim to say the least. As usual the money situation wasn't good, no change there then. It was just as well Jill had paid off our outstanding bills from the last good win. I decided to pay my old friend Jacob a visit, we sat talking for an hour or so then I left. For the first time in our lives Jill and I had started to argue over any and every little thing, this forced me to seek the company of one or two of my old mates at the Pig and Whistle, Simon's pub. I'd been frequenting the place for about three to four days when who should walk in, none other than Herman the German.

"Well, Well, Well," said Herman, that familiar evil grin on his smug ugly face. "Here tu drown yer sorrows Watson after yer run of bad luck? Oh-- I'd forgot yer don't drink, only real men drink and you're not a real man, are yer" "Am as much a man as you and maybe more," I replied.

One or two customers stepped back expecting the worst. "Yer a crap dog trainer Watson and al bet yer can't hold yer liquor," said Herman a great smirk on his smarmy face.

"Wrong on both counts, Herman, firstly ah can train a dog as good as anybody, maybe not better, but just as good, and as for drinking, just because ah don't drink doesn't mean ah can't."

I was just about to finish off my sentence when Herman interrupted. "Your first count on training a dog is rubbish, you've done yer money on that second rate hound of yours three times--- and ah still say yer can't hold yer ale."

I'd taken just about all I could take from that scumbag. "Right Mr big mouth, my dog Lucky against your dog, that's if you've got a dog, which ah doubt, then we'll have tu see who's the best drinker." "Hold on there little feller, lets get things in the right order and sort this business out once and for all, in front of all these witnesses." Most of them must have been thinking, Tom's bitten off a bit too much this time.

Herman stood in the middle of the room kicking over one or two chairs to show his authority. "You all heard him, his dog Lucky against my dog," Herman paused for a second or two before he announced the name of his dog---- *"Just Black."* There were gasps around the room.

"Shit," I said out aloud, to the delight of Herman and his cronies.

"Problem Watson," asked Herman a smirk stretching from ear to ear. "Get on with it Herman, you've got the chair."

"Now that the match is made with the dogs," said Herman, lets get on with the drinking side of it, what's yer poison Watson." "Vodka," I replied. "Vodka," repeated Herman, "Ah didn't have yer down as a Vodka man Watson." "Yer didn't have me down as a dog trainer either, is there a problem with the drinking side for you?"

Herman looked at me then fixed his eyes on the dozen or so men that were left in the pub.

"You behind the bar, yes you, pointing at Simon," Simon in turn pointing to himself. "Beer for me and vodka for him." This went on until we'd both had five drinks. I was beginning to slide from the upright position to being halfway under the table. "Had enough Watson," said Herman as his nose got to within six inches of my face.

"Before you slide all the way under that table Watson and get to drunk tu understand what's going on, lets get this business sorted."

"The winner of the match race gets both dogs, *right,* as soon as those two dogs cross the winning line they belong tu the man who's dog finishes first, understood Watson." "Yes sur," I slurred.

"He's pissed boss, doesn't know what the hell he's saying." "Not true you big ape," I pointed to one of Herman's burly minders who was just about to land one on my nose. "Wait yer fool," said Herman, a glint in his eye.

147

"Av got him just where ah want him, this is my chance tu get rid of him and his Jewish friend all in one go."

"Watson," he prodded with his finger. "Can yer hear Watson." "Yep sure can," I replied. "How about a little side bet, just tu make it more interesting." "Like what," I said as I slipped another inch or two under the table. "Like a £1,500 bet against your house, winner takes all." I was stunned into near soberness.

"My house, that's the roof over my kids heads, the only thing av got that's paid for, yer must think am crackers as well as half- pissed." "Yer always said he was chicken boss," said the minder, desperate for his boss to give the order to give me a crack. If there was anything in the world I hated it was being belittled and called *chicken* I'd rather receive the biggest hiding of my life than walk away from a fight, but this wasn't a fight, what the hell was I doing, "No bet," I said out loudly shaking my head. "Tu much tu lose Herman, tu much." Herman eager tu seal the bet barked. "Barman two more drinks, and make it quick."

Simon hurried over with the drinks, Herman downed his drink in one go. "Your turn Watson, or are yer gunner be beat on the drinking side as well," he snarled. I lifted the glass and struggled to drink it all down. Herman repeated the order and downed his beer in the usual way, straight down that big mouth of his.

I felt I was slowly sliding beneath the table and spilled half the contents of my glass. "Chick, Chick, Chick," came the cry from a minder. By this time I'd had enough. "Right, Right, Right," I screamed holding my hands to my head, "Al do it, ok, al do it." "Make him sign it boss, make him sign it in front of all these witnesses, cos when he leaves here and

148

wakes up in the morning he'll deny all what's gone on, make him sign boss." Herman looked hard and long at his man. "For once Lofty, yer could be right, hey you behind the bar, pen and paper and be quick about it."

Simon scurried off to the back room and returned with a notepad and pen, shaking like a leaf as he handed it to Herman. "Right Watson, you are gunner write this and sign it, then nobody can say it's been forged, right." I nodded in reply.

I started writing it just as Herman dictated, the house was his, the dog was his, that was if he was the winner of the race. I was also instructed to write that as soon as the winning dog crossed the line the bet was complete, the victor would take the spoils. I think Herman's reason for this was he was worried Jill might want to take the dog and cause a scene. I thought to myself if anything, Jill would want to keep the house! That's if the worst happened.

"There's one more thing ah want tu put in this letter Herman." "What's that loser," he replied. "It's that Simon gets your half share of this pub back." Herman and his cronies looked shocked that I knew about the deal between him and Simon.

Herman stared at me looking more menacing than ever--- "Why not Watson, you've got no chance of winning anyway," he said as he and his men laughed out loudly. The clause was scribbled onto the notepaper by my now shaking hand and duly signed.

"Your turn now," I said, shoving the pen and paper towards Herman's hand. He seemed to be in a trance, just staring at the paper, it seemed to last forever and I started to wonder if this was all a dream. No such luck, as we were both startled at the sound of breaking glass coming from the kitchen. "Lofty see what the hell's going on back there." Before anyone moved Simon appeared apologising. "It's --- It's just me, sorry—sorry, dropped a few glasses, sorry," he repeated.

"When this bet is won mister barman, things are gunner change yer can take my word on that," growled Herman.

"Are yer signing this paper or not, or du yer want tu call the bet off," I asked. "It's up tu you, it's your mouth that's been rabbiting on about this bet, or maybe you've got cold feet, it's up tu you." Where my courage was coming from standing up tu Mr big I'll never know, must have been the drink? But whatever it was shocked Herman into picking up the pen and snatching at the paper.

"Why has my signature got tu be on here Watson," he demanded. "Because if you want tu win what av got, the house etc. if there's no name on the paper who's gunner collect the bet?"

"He's right boss," said Lofty nudging his boss's hand towards the paper. Herman signed, Peter Chapman. "No, no boss, you've got tu sign yer proper name or it doesn't count, you'll not win the bet."

"That is me proper name yer thick head," barked Herman as he gave Lofty a thump in the ear. "Sorry Boss, ah thought it was always Herman, how was ah supposed tu know that it was Peter Chapman?"

"One more thing Herman, a copy of this paper is tu be kept by each one of us, just tu be on the safe side, if ah were you ad keep it in a safe place."

A copy was quickly made and duly signed by each one of us. I had finally slid from the chair as the cavalry arrived in the shape of Billy and Jimmy the beard. "Walter Dixon said yer were in here stoned out of yer mind, what the hell are yer playing at," said Billy, shaking his head in disbelief at the drunken state I was in.

Herman stood up and thrust the signed paper into Billy's face, his minders by his side expecting trouble.

Billy and the Beard hastily read the note and shook their heads then looked over to Herman.

"How the hell have yer got him tu sign this--Jill will kill him," said Billy. "If he doesn't pay up on the bet, she won't have to tu kill him, we will kill him for her, that's not a threat bonny lad, it's a *promise*, one more thing," Herman said as he turned to walk away.

"Tell Watson--- when he comes round, that the draw for the trap will take place at the traps just before the race, av heard about his little tricks placing lino in the bottom of the traps covered with a little sand to make sure his opposition doesn't get the best of starts, well tell him he's been rumbled and no matter what traps the dogs draw, my dog is wearing my favourite colour, Blood Red, number one."

"Why don't yer just take his house and dog now, yer seem tu have everything else in yer favour," said the Beard."Just a matter of time boys, just a matter of time, oh by the way, the race is next week, just in case the little man forgets." Billy and the Beard picked me up then carried me to the car. I must have looked a right mess as they placed my arms around their shoulders and walked me down the garden path into the house.

"What the hell's happened, is he all right Bill, has he been in an accident," screamed Jill in a panic. "Is he hurt." "No just drunk," replied Bill as I felt myself falling onto the couch.

"But Tom doesn't drink," said Jill as she proceeded to smack my face.

"What's brought all this on Billy, Tom, getting into a state like this." "Read this Jill," said Jimmy handing Jill the piece of paper, apparently Jill's eyes nearly popped out of their sockets with shock.

"He's either been drunk when he's signed it, or signed it then got drunk, either way it's done." "Done," said Jill, as she crumpled up the paper. "Anyway who the hell is this Peter Chapman?" Jimmy looked at Billy. "Tell her Bill, go on, tell her." Jill screamed at the top of her voice. "For Gods sake somebody bloody tell me before ah go out of me mind."--- "Herman the German"---said Billy and Jim together. Jill turned pale and sat down in the easy chair, her hand covering her mouth. "Herman is back," she mumbled, trying not to believe it as she sat there shaking her head. "You---you mean tu tell me--- that, that piece of human scum will own my *house* next week." Jill stood up then dashed in the direction of the toilet, you could hear her heaving her poor guts out.

By this time I'd started to recover, at the worst time I might add, Jill was just coming from the bathroom.

"Tom Watson," she said, you get this sorted by tomorrow, or the kids and me are gone. I lifted my head and was about to say something, then dropped straight off to sleep again. "When he wakes up Bill, give him this message, he's not tu come near me or the kids until this mess is sorted out, av done with him, any man that can gamble the roof over his kids heads is not worth calling a *man.*"

Jill gathered some clothes together and bundled the kids into the van. "Run me up tu me mother's Bill, he'll not be wanting the van in his state, then yer can bring it back, I don't want him coming up me mother's giving me hassle."

Two days had gone by and still no sign of Jill or the kids, it was driving me crazy, I'd never ever been parted from Jill or the kids since we were married. I was spending most of my time up at the Kennels with Billy and Jimmy the beard, with an occasional visit down to Jacob's shop while the lads kept an eye on Lucky, just in case we had a visit from Herman.

With the days dragging and still no sign of Jill, I was going mad. The village was rife with rumours that she'd ran off with some old school mate from way back, or I'd got myself a fancy woman.

One thing the village did have right and that was the race at the weekend, apparently they were going to come in from all over the place to see the biggest race to take place in these parts that anyone could remember.

Most of the folks were hoping to see a miracle, that Herman's dog Just Black, might get beat and rid the village of a tyrant and his cronies once and for all.

I'd decided to kill a bit of time and drive down to the track at Downhill to see Mr and Mrs Ryan about the arrangements for the match race at the weekend.

"Nice tu see yer young Tom," said Mr Ryan. "But its sad tu hear der problems yer having so it is."

"Has der Misses not come back den Tom," asked Mrs Ryan, a sympathetic look on her chubby face.

"Afraid not Mrs Ryan," I replied. "She say's she's not coming back."

"Ah go way wit cher," said Mrs Ryan. "Av left dis feller," pointing to her husband, "More times dan dis hare has been round dis track so ah have, is dat right Patrick, Patrick," she yelled as her husband turned slowly towards her.

"Am just tinking Mrs, how many times dis old hare has been round der track so I am, yer could be right Mrs, we just might have been apart dat many times so we might," as he gave his wife a sly wink.

"Best of luck Tom me lad for dis weekend and we hope tings will turn out right fer der Misses and yer good self so we do, God Bless," said Mrs Ryan. I was just about to leave when Mr Ryan called me back.

"Tom I was just remembering, ah had visit from Mr Herman so ah did, nothing heavy mind you, just a word tu say dat he'd be checking der traps himself so he would, now what would he be doing dat for?" He removed his hat to scratch his head. "It's a long story Mr Ryan, nothing for you tu worry about," I assured him as I walked out of the track.

The next three days up to race day seem to fly. In a funny way I was hoping this day would never come, here I was, sitting in my little terrace house that Jill and I had built up from a hovel to maybe lose it on a bloody dog race, who the hell could blame Jill for leaving me. A cold shiver ran down my spine with the thought of not just losing the house and the dog, but Jill and the kids too.

I must have been deep in thought when a banging on the door made me jump, shit I thought to myself, this can't be Billy or Jimmy, they would have come straight in. I peeped round the side of the curtain expecting one of Herman's heavies to be there. I was relieved when I saw this figure with arms outstretched clutching this large box and kicking at the bottom of the door.

JW had called in with enough meat to feed an army. Cuts of

beef, sausages, pies, pork joints and even some cuts for Lucky and the rest of the dogs.

"That should keep yer going for a while me old mate," said JW as he placed the huge box onto the kitchen table. JW his real name was Jim, the same as Jimmy the beard, but to avoid confusion it was shortened to JW. "Some cracking pies there Tom get stuck in, still *hot* in more ways than yer think," he said with a sly cheeky wink. "Cup of tea Jim," I asked as we emptied the contents of the box onto the table. "No time Tom, work tu be done, meat tu steal, ah mean borrow." That was JW he'd have the meat from the pies before the baker had them in the oven if he got the chance.

If he lost his job, half the village would starve. "Must dash Tom, get meself finished, van washed out ready for tu night, don't worry Tom, al see yer in a couple of hours at the track."

JW had reminded me of what little time was left, the old stomach was starting to churn. I'd never felt as tense and as nervous in my whole life, my body was a wreck shaking like a leaf, I was starting to have doubts about the whole thing, I didn't honestly know if I could go through with it, I was a wreck!

I made myself a cup of tea to try to settle the nerves and ate half a pie. It was no good, my stomach was so nervous that I had to make a dash for the bathroom as the pie and myself parted company.

Jimmy the beard and Billy had kept watch at the kennels, taking it in turns to stay overnight. I'd wanted to sleep at the kennels myself, but the lads thought it best if I stayed at the house, just in case Jill and the kids came back.

The clock in the living room struck seven, every chime was like a knife in my back and I was glad to see the lads

155

walking down the path with Lucky wagging his tail looking quite happy, at least one of us was in a good mood.

Everything was set for the biggest gamble of my life and the tension wasn't getting any easier. *Come on Watson, pull yourself together I said to myself as I paced up and down the room.*

I took a deep breath, filled my chest and said, "Right lets do it." Billy took the dog lead we used for Spotty that was hanging by the side of the door. "Just for luck Tom, just for luck." Billy was right we were going to need all the luck we could muster. Billy walked up the garden path, the Beard right behind him. I took one long last look round the house before locking it up----maybe for the last time.

"Come on Tom," said the Beard, "No time for sentiment, we've a race tu run." He was right; there was no turning back. We arrived at the car park and found it nearly full, the rumours were right everyone and their mother must have turned up to see this race. The Ryan's must have been over the moon with the amount of people squeezing in through that single turnstile.

Billy had decided to stay in the van with Lucky, while the Beard and myself went into the track. "Bbbbb beesst of luluck Ttom," said Mrs Moffit, "Shhhops ccclosed ffor the nnight, wwouldn't mmis tthis ffor the wworld." I thanked her and tried to make my way to the traps. You could hardly move, complete strangers shook my hand to wish me the best of luck.

We finally got to the traps to be greeted by Mr Ryan who quickly pointed out that Herman had being making enquiries as to my whereabouts.

"Turned up then Watson, what a surprise," came this voice

from the crowd; there was no mistaking who it belonged to.

Herman and his heavies had pushed their way through the packed crowd, no matter who got in their way or who got hurt, woman, kids, they'd all got the same treatment.

There was one more race before Lucky and Just black would decide my fate. Mr Ryan advised Herman and myself to bring our dogs in through the back entrance to avoid the dogs being injured walking through the crowd.

I was just about to set off for the dog when Herman grabbed my arm. "Not you Watson," he said, "Send your man with the beard, you stay here where ah can keep an eye on yer."

Mr Ryan politely, but gingerly stepped in between us. "Now now gentlemen, let's not be having any trouble at dis stage of der racing, let's not be doing any ting stupid lads."

Herman loosened his vice like grip on my arm. I could see Billy and Herman's man making their way towards the traps with the dogs. My heart was pounding, stomach churning, was I glad that I'd only eaten half of that pie.

There was an almighty roar from the crowd as the two dogs neared the traps. This was it, my fate was about to be decided, my mouth was dry, my whole body felt as if it was just going to collapse. *Come on Watson, I said to myself, don't let a scumbag like Herman get to you.* I shrugged my shoulders, stretched my neck and said to myself, this is it; if you're going down, go down with a bit of dignity.

"Right Mr Ryan, you can toss the coin tu see what traps the dogs will be starting from." "Just a minute Watson," said Herman as he approached the traps.

"I'm checking all of the traps before any coin is tossed, I'm not taking any chances with you Watson."

157

Herman examined every trap, inch-by-inch, top bottom sides, the lot as he had done a couple of days previously. Mr Ryan was bemused. "If yer can be telling me what it is you'll be looking for Mr Herman, maybe ah can be helping yer so ah will!"

"Mind yer own business old man and toss the coin, I'm having *Heads* in more ways than one," he laughed. Mr Ryan then tossed the coin in the air, caught it, and then placed it on the back of one hand concealing it with the other. "You er called heads Mr Herman," holding out his hands at full stretch for the result to be uncovered.

Mr Ryan slowly removed his hand. "*Tails,*" he announced, Herman lunged forward to check for himself, then turned the coin over, just to make sure it had a head on the other side.

"That's the only thing you'll win tu night Watson, pick yer trap and be prepared tu lose everything you've got."

The dogs were coated up with their walking out coats and their racing colours underneath. With a slight drizzle falling and a thin fine mist, it was like one of those films when someone was about to suffer a grim fate.

Herman had chosen the Red jacket number one, by all accounts his favourite colour, it reminded him of blood he would boast, and not his own I hasten to add.

We had chosen the Orange jacket number five. "Come on Watson," snarled Herman. "Pick yer trap, not that it'll make any difference, you've tried tu beat Just Black three times, and come unstuck, tuday won't make any difference, pick your trap."

"Not tu confuse things we are wearing the orange jacket, Lucky will run from trap five, I presume you'll be taking the one box, the Red." "You bet Watson," replied Herman.

"My dog comes from any trap, but trap one is his favourite, that's the second mistake you've made tuday Watson--- your first was turning up."

You could hear muttering among the punters. "Why the hell has Tom picked the five trap, he must be mad." It may have looked that way to them, but I had my reasons, right or wrong, all was in order for the race to start. Mr Ryan had taken up his post in the Judge's box ready to drive the hare. He had just started the announcement to place the dogs into the traps when he suddenly stopped.

A fight had broken out among the crowd. It must have raged for at least five or six minutes before things settled down. Mr Ryan was looking concerned that the spectators might spill over onto the track and injure themselves, when it was over Mr Ryan proceeded with the business in hand.

"Place dem dogs in der traps gentlemen if yer please," came the announcement. This really was it, my stomach in knots and my hands out of control shaking with both fear and excitement. I could hear the bookmakers shouting the odds of 5-1 Lucky, 1-5 Just Black. The odds from the bookies didn't help my confidence, not that it made any difference now the hare was running. It flashed past the traps with both dogs coming out on equal terms.

The dogs had run about two hundred yards with the five dog just leading into the bend, neck and neck stride for stride the dogs matched each other it was almost unbearable to watch.

I could hear a familiar voice above the rest of the crowd screaming for trap five, the unmistakeable voice of Jill my wife. Both dogs were racing round the last bend, only one hundred and fifty yards to the winning line with the orange jacket showing just a length in front, the crowd were going mad shouting for the five jacket to pass the post first, the excitement was unbelievable, the dogs had crossed the winning line with trap five two lengths clear of the red jacket. A feeling of relief flooded through my nerve wracked body. I could still hear Jill screaming with enjoyment even after the race had finished.

"Der result of der match race Ladies and Gent's is First number five Lucky." A tremendous roar went up from the crowd that seemed to go on forever. " Will yer not be settling down now, ah can hardly hear meself tink," said Mr Ryan continuing with the result. "Second number One, Just Black, distance 2 lengths and a new track record tu go wit dat of 26-14. The crowd cheered again then suddenly went very quiet. Herman was on the track marching towards me Billy and the dogs.

"Watson," shouted Herman, with a look that could kill on his face, I was expecting fire to burst from his flared nostrils at anytime.

"Watson you little shit, you've cheated me, ah don't know how you've done it, but it's done yer no good yer little waster, both dogs are mine, and yer house, yer didn't think for a moment that if yer won the bet that ad pay yer." By this time the crowd had gone completely silent, everyone could hear Herman's threats. Their hopes and dreams of a Herman rid village were quickly diminishing. "What about the paper we both signed," I asked.

"What er-- paper would that be Watson," said Herman turning to one of his heavies. Have you seen any paper signed by me Lofty."

"Not me boss, just the racing paper with yer tips on it," he

160

quipped. Herman came closer looking very menacing. There was no way I was giving up the dogs or the house without a fight. I was preparing for the worst when a voice echoed from the crowd.

"Would this be the paper that seems to be in question," an outstretched arm in the air moved through the crowd towards the winning line. As the man came closer a look of fear could be seen on Herman's face. It was none other than my old mate Twitcher Murphy.

"You," he pointed at Herman. "Is this your signature?" Herman glanced at the piece of paper briefly and nodded his head. It was the first time I'd seen Herman for the coward that he really was. I had a hunch that if things didn't go right for him, he would try to wriggle out of the bet---so I left my copy with my old mate Mr Murphy.

"Is this paper going to be honoured Mr," asked Twitcher menacingly as he stood toe to toe looking up into Herman's fear filled eyes. "Of course Twi," Herman just avoiding the biggest mistake of his life when he nearly called Harry, Twitcher.

"Ah was just kidding when ah said that ah was taking the dogs and the house, isn't that right Tom." A resounding "*No* and a shake of my head, was my reply.

"That being the case Herman, where's the mans money? Fifteen hundred quid it says on here, if you were only er--- kidding as you say, you'll have the money on yer, isn't that right," said Twitcher holding out his hand for the money. "Well Harry it's like this, ah thought with a big crowd here tunight the money might get nicked, some bad people about."

"Yer right Herman, real bad people, starting with *you*."

161

"It's, It's not like that Harry honest," stuttered Herman in near panic.

"Is that gorilla with you," asked Twitcher pointing to Lofty. Herman nodded, "He's got till the next race is over to get that £1,500 back here---if he doesn't make it, he'll be looking for a new boss, I only hope you've been treating him good Herman, he might not come back, so just to make sure he doesn't get light fingered and forgets to come back with the money, I'll send my boy Tony to keep him company." Herman gave Lofty a bunch of keys and spoke discreetly in his ear.

"Lofty get back here pronto, the last time Twitcher Murphy sent somebody on a similar errand and they were late, it was for *their* boss four fingered Gibson, Twitcher was the reason he only had four fingers tu start with, his body hasn't been found yet, *Nor has his minder."*

"Yer wasting time Herman and *you* know I like punctuality, ask four fingers Gibson--- that is if you can find *him.*" said Twitcher, a broad smile on his face. As soon as Herman's minder got the message he was off like a shot, if the gate had been closed I'm sure he'd have gone straight through it.

True to his word, Herman's man delivered the cash on time, assisted by Tony. God knows where the money came from at such short notice but who cares, it was too late to go to the bank, even with the mask and gun.

Twitcher counted out the money in front of Herman, just to make sure it was all there and that there was no funny money amongst it. He then took Herman to one side, they were in deep discussion for three to four minutes. By this time Herman was looking a distinctive pale colour.

"You've done all right Tom," said Twitcher his twitch starting to settle after his little discussion with Herman. "If ah didn't have your help Harry, ah wouldn't be standing here with £1,500 in me hand."

"Yer right Tom, but ah wouldn't be standing here with a few quid in me pocket meself, ah just had this funny feeling that yer might just pull this little caper off and ah was right, so ah had a good bet on Lucky tu win. How yer did it Tom is your business and the best of luck ter yer." He started walking away then he shouted back, "By the way Tom, ah don't think you'll have any more trouble from the German, Av persuaded him tu go back tu the Fatherland or somewhere similar, either way, *he's been warned.*"

Billy and Jimmy the beard headed off home with the two dogs, I stayed behind a little while to see if I could find Jill and the kids, but there was no such luck, they were nowhere to be found.

I finally fought my way out of the track having been slapped on the back and congratulated by nearly everyone I bumped into. I was being thanked not just for winning the race, but also for being responsible for the demise of the most hated man in the North East, and that gave me great satisfaction. The feeling was good, but I still had that emptiness of not having Jill and the kids around me.

It wasn't long before JW pulled up with a smile from ear to ear. "Jump in Tom I'll run yer up home." He pulled up outside the gate then sped off like a man being chased by a scorned lover.

I stood there staring at the house that could have been lost and thought what a massive gamble I'd pulled off, and how horribly wrong it could have gone.

163

Walking down that path to an empty house was awful. A chink of light shone through the partly drawn curtains, Billy must have left the light on by mistake, I said to myself.

Things didn't feel the same without Jill and the kids, I was just about to turn round and pop down to the Pig and Whistle when I heard the door open slowly. Shit I thought to myself, maybe Herman had sent one of his heavies to grab back the £1,500 and was hiding in the house. I turned on my toe's and was just about to jump the gate when a voice shouted, "Tom Watson, before yer think of jumping that gate and maybe crippling yer self in the process, you've got some serious explaining tu do."

This was the first time I'd seen Jill in over a week and how I'd missed her and the kids. Her silhouette in the doorway reminded me of just how much that had been. I was just about to fling my arms around her and give her a big squeeze, when she turned and went into the house.

"Tom Watson," she said pointing her finger aggressively at me. "You have put me through hell this past week, wondering if you were all right and managing tu make yer meals--- wondering if ah was still going to have a roof over me head."

Jill wasn't half steaming, I was now sitting in the easy chair looking up at the woman I loved and thought -- she doesn't half look a little cracker when she's mad.

She'd thrown just about all the abuse she could think of when I stood up and said, "You've missed me Jill Watson, haven't yer?" She stood there looking all flustered, running out of words to say, she was so agitated she took a kick at the table leg, then turned once more to me. "You, you, swine Tom Watson, yer don't know how much I've missed yer, even me mother's missed yer, the kids have being going mad

164

tu come down tu the house tu see yer."

"Jill, it was your idea tu leave, ah thought yer might have had a little more faith in me, du yer really think ad let that Herman take the roof from over the kids heads?"

Jill stood there, tears welling up in her eyes. "Ah should have known yer had something up yer sleeve Tom, but it was everything that happened that day, we'd had words, yer got drunk, what did yer expect!" She was becoming more and more upset, it was time to come clean and tell her everything. "Sit down sweetheart and I'll tell yer the story right from the very beginning, if yer want tu interrupt at any time feel free tu do so." That was something I was to regret saying. I was just about to start, when Jill asked why I'd got myself drunk. My reply was, *"I didn't."* "But yer were drunk, Billy and the beard had tu bring yer home in a right state." "No Jill, ah was pretending tu be drunk." "But," she interrupted once again. "Joe Moss said he was down at the Pig and Whistle and yer must have had half a dozen vodka's at least."

"That's what Joe Moss thought ---- and so did Herman and everyone else."

"But," she interrupted once again. "Everybody saw yer drinking glasses of vodka," she said, a puzzled look on her tear stained face. "Everyone thought they saw me drinking vodka, it was glasses of *water* with a touch of something in it to make it smell like vodka." "How the hell did yer manage that, Herman was apparently sitting less than two feet from yer seat," she said, as she grew more and more frustrated. "First of all I found out that vodka has very little smell."

"That might be so Tom Watson and av heard about Jesus making water into wine, but how the hell did yer turn vodka into water?" "Easy," I replied. "With the help of Simon,

Simon, just kept the phoney drinks coming and ah did the rest by pretending to get drunk--- that was the only way tu trap Herman --- and it worked a treat."

"That explains the drinks Tom, but how did yer get Simon tu go along with that, ah thought he was terrified of Herman," she said. "He was, more terrified than what yer could imagine."

"What sort of terrified," she said as she settled herself on the settee all eyes and ears.

I started to tell Jill the whole gruesome story, that when Simon's father died and left the pub to his only son. Herman found out that Simon was batting for the other side. "Wait there Tom, just hold yer horses," she said, one of those curious looks on her face.

"You've got me lost here Tom, what du yer mean batting for the other side?" "Have ah got tu spell it out Jill, Simon was *queer, he was putting the key in the back door!*" I could see she was just about to query my explanation again when I stopped her.

"Simon prefers the company of other men--- not women." Jill looked a little shocked then said. "Got yer Tom," she nodded as she made herself more comfortable, kicking off her shoes and pulling her legs onto the settee.

"Carry on Tom." "Thanks," I replied and carried on with the story.

"Herman took full advantage of knowing Simon was queer and threatened to tell the whole village, he also made him sign over half the pub, his price for remaining silent."

"So what," said Jill, "If Simon's queer it's not the end of the world." "Yer right Jill," I replied as I hesitated with my next few words wondering how best I could explain.

"It's—It's not the end of the world sweetheart ---- *But* when you're being forced into sex with a monster like Herman, It's not something you'd want the village to know about."

Jill stood up from the settee, gob-smacked, as she stood there with her mouth wide open. "Herman ---Herman," she repeated. "That brute of a man Queer, and for him to force himself on a nice quiet lad like Simon is disgusting, it makes me want tu throw up, in fact, *hu, hu* excuse me."

Jill ran to the toilet I could hear her heaving from the pit of her stomach. I was trying to act all macho by not wanting to throw up myself, but how long could I keep up the pretence. Jill returned looking as white as sheet.

"O.K sweetheart," I asked. "Don't you bloody sweetheart me Tom Watson, after what you've just made me do, it's disgusting, but it does explain Simon's quietness of late and why he was always looking over his shoulder as if there was somebody there!"

I sat there dumbfounded, speechless, how the hell could she blame me for her being sick! "Well," she said, urging me to get on with the story by throwing one of the small cushions from the settee into my lap. "Well, how did yer win that race," she asked, the colour in her face slowly starting to return.

"Ah just don't believe Lucky could beat Herman's dog in a straight run race, ah just don't believe it Tom," she said shaking her head in disbelief. "Get yerself comfy on that settee and al tell yer how we won the race."

"The first bit you already know, with the involvement of Simon and the drinks." "Av heard enough of Simon thanks, get on with the rest of it Watson, was it Lucky that won that race?"---- "*No.*" "Ah knew, ah knew Lucky couldn't beat that dog, ah just knew it, so how the hell did yer do it."

"With a lot of planning and hard work, starting with old Jacob," I replied. "Yer mean Jacob was in on this scheme as well," she said looking more shocked than ever.

"Yes, Jacob was one of the main contributors."

"That's why yer kept going missing, yer were going down tu Jacob's shop?" "Correct," I replied. "Jacob was making some special racing jackets." Jill interrupted once more. "Unless they had bloody wings on them Tom they couldn't make Lucky win that race."

"All in good time Jill, patience my dear, patience--- as Jacob would say in his soft Jewish voice," I carried on with the story.

"Herman had specifically chosen the red jacket number one, that was a great start for us, we new what colour jacket Herman's dog would be wearing on the day of the race."

"And," she said, prompting me with her head to carry on with the story.

"Jacob had some paper like material in his shop similar to what he and his comrades used when they were working in the sewing shops for the Germans."

"They would dress themselves like trustie prisoners in a uniform made from this material to fool the guards when moving from hut to hut, then discard it until another time." Jill was starting to get very impatient.

"Tom, get tu the point, just tell me how yer did it."

"Easy, you saw Herman's dog parade with the red jacket on---- and Lucky with the orange jacket, clear so far sweetheart." "As soon as Herman was satisfied the jackets were the correct colours, the dogs were coated up with their

168

walking out coats on, O.K." Jill nodded. "Carry on Mister, am listening."

"Well there was a fight in the crowd," I was just about to continue when once again Jill interrupted. "Don't tell me about fighting Tom Watson, it was Brendan and Stringvest." "Ah know who it was Jill--- it was me that told them tu start the fight in the first place." "Maybe so," said Jill, but al bet yer didn't tell them tu start fighting each other, they were knocking seven sorts of shi—well they were battering each other like it was a world championship fight, there was no stopping them."

I sat there wondering whether those numbskulls would ever get anything right. "They were supposed tu pick a fight with Herman's men, tu create a disturbance to attract Herman's attention away from the dogs."

"They did that alright Tom," said Jill, "There was more people watching them than watching the dogs, the worst thing about it was Brendan and Stringvest seemed tu be enjoying it."

"Well sweetheart I'll continue, while Laurel and Hardy were slugging it out between themselves, it gave us just enough time to take off the walking out coats and false racing jacket's all in one go, to reveal the opposite colours to what the dogs had on originally, this was done in one swift jerk, bearing in mind that the jackets were like a paper material, all removed in a flash before the dogs entered the traps." Jill looked a little puzzled.

"So Lucky had the red jacket on and ran out of the one box and Just Black had the orange jacket on from trap five----so Lucky *never* won that race, it was Just black." "Correct my little brain box," I said sarcastically, before having to defend myself from a barrage of missiles.

"You cheating little bas----so and so, but---but how did yer manage tu swap the jackets and the dogs with Herman's man standing there?" "That Jill, was all done on the morning of the race, it would have been a major, major problem, but thanks tu you, my little darling, we were able to pull it off."

Jill sat there looking quite smug tossing her head lightly in appreciation.

"Well am glad av been some use in this er, well planned job Mr Watson, so what great part did ah play," she asked looking quite pleased with herself. "Remember the fight outside Jacob's shop, when Brendan took on Herman's men and laid two or three of them out." "Yer ah remember," she said nodding her head. "Well one of the three received a good bashing from Brendan plus a good kicking from Herman." "If yer remember we had tu phone for the ambulance."

"Ah remember," said Jill. "Well, Herman's man never forgot the help you gave him that day, if you can also recollect the words he spoke to you Jill, they were, *IF EVER AH CAN DO YER A FAVER MRS, AH WILL,* that favour was called in on the day of the race."

I also explained to Jill that it had transpired that Herman had demoted and belittled his man to a general lackey, giving him a pittance of a wage and menial work in the kennels. The man was waiting for the day that he could have his revenge. He had not forgotten the good turn you did for him, and when he heard about the match race he came looking for me to see if he could help in any way.

He also told me that Herman was responsible for the death of the rest of Lucky's litter the day Billy and I discovered the sack containing Lucky and his dead brothers and sisters.

170

Herman had ordered the drowning of all the pups just for spite, that is all but one---Just Black, as we know him today, Lucky's brother. The man who bred the litter owed Herman money and just couldn't pay, Herman agreed with the man to have one of the pups as part payment, but the evilness in this devil couldn't bear to think that he may have left the best pup behind, so he had the rest of the litter stolen just to make sure. Had it not been for old Ben that day by the riverside he would have succeeded with his evil deed, thanks to the old dog we have Lucky.

Jill sat there, tears rolling down her face as I told her the story. "Come here yer great lump," she said to me as her tear stained face rubbed next to mine. "Tom Watson you promise me you'll never put me through this sort of thing again and go behind my back."

"There's one more thing Jill---ah have gone behind yer back, have a luck through the curtains." Jill gingerly moved one side of the curtains and jumped back in shock. "Tom, the gardens full of people, who the hell's out there."

Little did Jill know that I'd arranged for all our friends to meet back at our house as a surprise, that's if all had gone well, and for Doris to persuade Jill to come down to the house in the first place. If things hadn't gone well, God knows what would have happened?

By this time Jill was like a cat on hot bricks peering from behind the curtains into the darkness of the garden. "Who are they Tom," she asked, a puzzled look on her face. "Best open the door tu find out sweetheart." "You---You, Tom, you open it." Jill stood back while I opened the door. "Mam, Dad, what are you doing here." Before they could answer the kids barged in, followed by Billy, Jimmy the beard, JW, Simon and old

Jacob, I was just about to close the door when in trooped Brendan, Willie, Maxine and Anytime Annie, followed by Tommy the cap. I was just about to go inside when I saw the headlights of a car and heard the screeching of tyres pulling up outside the house, then the noise of a car door slamming as it screeched off.

Bloody idiots I said to myself, probably drunken louts.

I was just about to close the door when I heard a faint moan coming from the direction of our privet hedge.

"Who's there I shouted," a low painful groan and a slight movement drew my attention to a corner at the top of the garden.

A faint voice called out my name. I stooped down for a closer look, I wasn't sure but it looked like Herman's kennel man Monty. I shouted into the house for Billy to bring out a torch, what I discovered when I shone the light onto the man's body shocked and sickened me.

It was Monty, he'd been so badly beaten he was hardly recognisable, when Billy and I tried to lift him his screams of pain brought out the rest of the guests. Brendan was first, followed by Jill and kids.

"Get those kids back into the house Jill, quick." "Why," asked Jill." "Because ah bloody well say so, now do it."

Jill did a quick about turn and ushered the kids back into the house. No matter what part of Monty's body you touched, there was pain and blood. I gently lifted up one of his arms to try to help him into the house.

What I saw when I glanced down through the fading torchlight both shocked and physically turned my stomach. I turned and started to puke uncontrollably. Brendan grabbed hold of Monty's blood stained body to prevent him from falling, I was no good to anyone, kneeling on all fours throwing up.

Billy and Brendan carried Monty, screaming in agony over to the light of the door where his injuries were more apparent. Brendan gasped in horror as he lifted one of the mans arms. "Be Jesus," he screamed, "Somebody's cut off der mans hand so der have." On closer examination by Jacob, the man had lost four fingers.

Even in tremendous pain Monty was still trying to speak, trying to whisper something. Jill shouted from the house that the ambulance was on its way.

Jacob was used to attending to people injured like this, unlike like me my stomach couldn't take it.

"Tom my boy, the man is faintly saying something about the dog's." Jacob tried to comfort him the best way he could. "Rest my friend, help is on the way," he assured him. Billy, the lads and me looked at each other then ran straight over to the van and headed off full speed to the kennels.

If this was Herman's work, the damage he'd inflicted on poor Monty was nothing to what he might do to two helpless animals.

We arrived at the kennels to be greeted by a note pinned to the door with a blood stained knife, it read. *You may have won the race Watson, and my money, but it's me that's got the last laugh, the dogs have gone tu that big racetrack in the sky, tough.* The message ended with a bloodstained sign of a swastika

I had the worst feeling I've ever encountered in the pit of my stomach; it was as if someone was trying to pull out my innards with their bare hands.

I stood there, rooted to the spot, unable to move a muscle.

Billy and the Beard rushed past me to where Lucky and Just Black were kennelled. After no more than thirty seconds Billy came back shaking his head and looking as white as a sheet. "Don't go down there Tom," he begged. "It won't do yer any good."

I knew it was the wrong thing to do but I ignored Billy's advice and pushed past him to find the most horrific sight that I have ever seen in my life. To my horror, *both dogs had had their heads cut off and must have died an agonising death.*

Jimmy the beard had already left the kennel from the other door and started digging their graves.

He gave me a glance then just shook his head, tears mingling in his beard as he stood there in the light beaming from the kennel doorway. "It has tu be done Tom, no good waiting till morning when Jill and the kids are here, won't do anybody any good." "Jimmy's right Tom," said JW with a nod of agreement from Billy, there was nothing anyone could do.

I thought to myself, what the hell am I going to tell Jill and the kids, how am I going to explain this horrible mess.

There was only one thing I could do---*lie through my teeth.* The lads and I talked it over and came up with a story that the dogs had been stolen, it wouldn't go down well with the kids or Jill, but what do you tell them, the dogs have had their heads cut off by a madman bent on revenge---- *I don't think so.*

The dogs were buried together, the freshly dug soil covered with a few old tin sheets.

Jill swallowed the story about the dogs been stolen and finding them again would be near impossible, especially as both dogs had no ear marks to identify them. News had soon spread around the village that the dogs had been stolen, not all were convinced, especially Mr Twister Murphy. He rang me a couple of weeks after the incident, there was no two way conversation and no questions asked, the only words spoken were from Twitcher----*"Some people never learn,"* then hung up.

It had been a devastating few months since the tragic loss of Lucky and Just Black, we never did find out the pet name of Lucky's brother, but deep down I knew neither dog would be forgotten. Only a handful of people knew what had happened on that tragic unforgettable night, one of the few was old Jacob.

He visited the kennels one day, which was very unusual to say the least. His excuse for the visit was a poor one.

"Tom my boy, how are things these days, Jill and the little ones, they are ok?" "To your first question Jacob, things could be better, to your second question, Jill and the kids are fine, but my question to you Jacob is, to what do we owe this unexpected pleasure."

"The shop Tom, she is very quiet, I think we need a break from each other maybe." For Jacob to leave that shop there had to be some other reason than the one he had just given to me. Jacob would be in that shop trying to drum up business in an earthquake.

I sat on the old wooden bench drumming my fingers on the armrest waiting for Jacob to come clean with the real reason for his visit; I didn't have to wait long.

"Tom," said the old man stroking his beard and looking very pensive over his old wire rimmed specs.

"A friend of mine who lives in the south of England called in to see me in my little shop, he was on his way to see Morry the money lender at the synagogue, we chatted for a while about the old times, then he produced an old newspaper from his pocket, I thought you might like to see it my friend."

Jacob showed me the newspaper, which had a very interesting story on the front page about a brutal murder near London, a man who had been beheaded.

His head had been placed beside his body. For some unknown reason there had been no attempt to hide the torso or the head.

A couple walking their greyhounds in woods outside London had made the grim discovery. There was no identification on the body, the only thing the police had to go on--- was an arrow shaped scar on his left cheek and the tattoo of a Swastika on each hand!

The police had found a note in the man's pocket with the scribbled words saying--- *You Were Warned.* Jacob looked at me with a mischievous grin and said, "You know Tom, the man upstairs, he moves in mysterious ways, this man they found in London could be?"--- Jacob stopped in mid sentence and shrugged his shoulders, *"Who knows who he might be Tom my boy?"* A look of satisfaction and a faint smile lit up his rugged face. I think both Jacob and myself knew who the dead man was and we took great pleasure and satisfaction knowing that an evil man had met his deserved end. It was pure coincidence that greyhound people had found the body. But for the body to be found the way it was didn't take a lot of working out. There was no trying to hide the scar on the man's face. There was no trying to hide the tattooed swastika on his hands. The culprits for reasons of their own wanted his identity to be *known.*

The game I had played with Herman was a dangerous one,

that could have gone drastically wrong at any time. Fortunately I still had my wife, kids and my house. The tragedy of it all was the great loss of Lucky and Just Black--- that is something that will live with me for the rest of my life. But the question I keep asking myself is.

WAS THERE *EVER REALLY* A WINNER?

Cystic Fibrosis

When my wife Iris and myself received the devastating news from my son Gil and his wife Karen that our Granddaughter Niki, eighteen months old had been diagnosed with Cystic Fibrosis, an incurable illness with a life's expectancy at that time of five to ten years, it was a terrible shock.

We were lucky to have enjoyed sixteen wonderful years with Niki, thanks to the dedicated C/F staff at Jimmy's hospital in Leeds who in my mind gave her those extra few years.

The only chance a child born with C/F has of extending their life is a transplant of the heart and lungs, which would extend their lives five to ten years. My family had no idea of what C/F was, or of the pain and heartache it would cause. Niki got on with her life and tried to live it to the full. With physiotherapy three times daily and numerous medication's there was never any self pity or complaint from her.

No matter what she attempted, dancing, horse riding, all sorts of activities, she would give it her all, with the full encouragement of her parents and the rest of her family. The day Niki died on the 9th of February, 2001, aged sixteen in hospital, a little piece of her family and friends died with her.

Without the encouragement from my granddaughter, our first book *RICH WITHOUT MONEY* would not have been written. It is through this encouragement and in her memory that we have penned a second book. *THE CRAZIEST GAMBLE.*

As with *Rich Without Money,* a donation from every book sold will go directly to the C/F ward at Jimmy's Hospital Leeds, to help make the lives of the C/F sufferers a little more comfortable. Our thanks go to everyone that has kindly bought a book.

Thanking You.
                    Trevor and Iris Liddle.